ON THE MAHOGANY TRAIL

ON THE MAHOGANY TRAIL

by Donald MacIntosh

EXCELLENT PRESS
LUDLOW

Excellent Press
Palmer's House
7 Corve Street
Ludlow SY8 1DB

A copy of the British Library Cataloguing in Publication Data
for this title is available from the British Library

ISBN 1 900318 14 8

Typeset by Dorwyn Ltd, Rowlands Castle, Hants
Printed in Great Britain

DEDICATION

For Paula,
who loves all nature, and in memory of
her husband
Dr Malcolm McDonald,
my friend
and
fellow Old Coaster

Acknowledgements

Gordon W. Nixon took the excellent photograph displayed on the cover of this book while working with me in Cameroon.

Much help and advice was given to me by Drs Joyce and Richard Lowe of the Nigerian Field Society. It should be emphasised, however, that any errors in tree nomenclature or information contained within these pages are entirely the fault of the author and have nothing to do with either of those two charming intellectuals and lovers of all things West African.

Gordon Martin, an Old Coaster and friend, whose extensive knowledge of the West African rainforests has made his advice in the writing of this book invaluable.

Last but by no means least, another well-known Old Coaster, Arthur Deaville, in appreciation of his constant encouragement.

Bibliography

Unwin, A. H.   *West African Forests and Forestry*. London, 1920

Schweitzer, Albert *More From the Primeval Forest*. A. & C. Black Ltd., 1931

Harley, George Way *Native African Medicine*. Cambridge, Massachusetts, 1941

Voorhoeve, A. G.   *Liberian High Forest Trees*. State Agricultural University, Wageningen, 1965

Contents

Prologue

WHEN DAVID BURNETT of Excellent Press suggested that I might devote some thought to attempting a book on African rainforest trees, I did not, at first, greet the suggestion with the degree of enthusiasm that might have been expected of a forester who had spent the happiest years of his life in those marvellous forests of West and Central Africa. I had, I considered, valid reasons for my caution. For one thing, I am no academic. I possess neither the desire nor the discipline required for the long, hard, concentrated grind of churning out a book of purely academic inclination. In any case, there are plenty of first-class books on the subject which, though for the most part buried in select archives around the country, are available on request to anyone holding a British Libraries ticket. I had no reason to believe that another one by a humble 'bushman' would contribute anything much to the collection.

I said as much to David. 'Then why', he persisted, 'don't you make this a totally different type of book? Write it in your own way, in a way that ordinary people can understand. Tell us about the forests as they were in your day. Tell us what the more interesting species looked like, the sort of conditions in which they grew, the creatures you most often found in association with individual species, the uses to which the forest people put each species you describe – what they did with the timber from them, the different sorts of medicines they extracted from the bark, the flowers, the fruits, the leaves . . .'

The more I thought about it, the more I liked the idea. Books on African trees have tended, more often than not, to be written for the university student or the professional dendrologist, and in language only perfectly understood by this elite minority. But what about the layman – the carpenter, the joiner, the builder, the D.I.Y. enthusiast, the chap whittling the hours away in his garden shed of a winter's night with the wind howling outside – who would like to know the background to the piece of timber on which he is currently working? The man who would like to know more about its origin, what the parent tree looked like, the conditions in which it grew, in fact, everything about it, explained in everyday language, without being drowned in a morass of incomprehensible scientific words and terms? To all but the dedicated botanist, there can be few things more off-putting than to read at the start of a chapter that tree regeneration of a particular species is 'diagnostic by the minutely stellate-puberulous hypocotyl'. It is surely of interest only to the specialist in wood technology and utilization to be told that the timber of a certain species is of a 'Wt. 1,000–1,030 kg/m3 and SG 1.03'. It might be over-simplifying things to write instead that, in the first example, the seedlings were covered in tiny hairs and, in the second, that the timber concerned was as heavy as hell. But it did seem to me that somewhere between the two extremes there lay an opportunity to write a tree book that would entertain as well as inform readers. With this book, I have attempted to do both.

Each chapter highlights a well-known timber species, and the first page of each chapter lists properties of that species which will be of interest mainly to the exporter and the sawmiller. But that is about as technical as it gets. For the most part, this is a book about the inhabitants – plant, animal and human – of the African rainforests as the author knew them when the world was young and he was younger.

If, in reading here about those great forests, the reader absorbs even a fraction of the joy that the writer experienced from living in them, then this book will have been well worth the effort.

Chapter 1

And in the Beginning

ALTHOUGH IT WAS well into the 20th century before the enormous potential of the timber species to be found in the forests of tropical Africa really began to attract the attentions of the outside world, for some considerable time before that there had been a sense of creeping disquiet spreading throughout the sheltered palatinates of the European timber industry. Even a hundred years earlier it had been obvious to anyone with half an eye that supplies of the traditional mahoganies from the Americas were fast drying up. They had been logged to near extinction. Substitutes had to be found, but where? The timber men took their time about it, scouring the world, looking for anything even remotely resembling the American mahoganies, their quest taking them to such unlikely habitats as the shores of the Orient and the fringes of the arid scrub savannahs of Western Australia.

It soon became apparent, though, that satisfactory replacements were not going to be all that easy to find. In desperation, the Europeans switched their attention to a land much nearer home. It was a part of the world known only to a handful of explorers, traders and missionaries. They were eccentrics almost without exception, but few were so eccentric as to venture far beyond the relative security of the ports already established along those murky shores, for beyond the ports lay the terrible unknown: dark impenetrable forests of sinister legend, of mystery, of gruesome voodoo rites, of strange and horrible sickness, and of death.

Especially, of death.

To the outside, this part of Africa was already known as 'The White Man's Grave'.

As a label, it was by no means exaggerated. 'Take care and beware the Bight of Benin, there's ten comes out for forty goes in,' was a piece of doggerel that had always been applicable to the Coast, particularly as far as white people were concerned. White prospectors, lured by tales of gold and diamonds and ivory, appeared on the Coast in small numbers throughout the 19th century. Many of these stayed permanently, too, under the hot red soils of ancient Africa, having succumbed in somewhat indecent haste to the unfriendly environment. Even at the end of the century that remarkable lady Mary Kingsley wrote in her book *Travels in West Africa* of the time when, on a visit to Accra in the Gold Coast, she found herself being conducted on an informal tour of the local European cemetery by a saturnine colonial officer who 'walked there every afternoon so as to get used to the place before permanently staying in it', as he so eloquently put it. 'We always keep two graves ready dug for Europeans,' he informed her lugubriously, 'for we know they will be occupied by nightfall.'

The greatest killer was malaria – *Mal'aria*, they called it in those days, from the Italian for 'foul air', because it was believed that the sickness was the result of inhaling the foetid swamp air of the coastal regions, especially at night. Even as late as Miss Kingsley's time, this was a commonly held belief. In Appendix 11 of her book she writes with characteristic irony: '. . . may I ask how you can do without air from 6.30 p.m. to 6.30 a.m.? or what other air there is but night air, heavy with malodorous exhalations, available then?'

By the middle of the 20th century few were in any doubt as to the identity of the insidious killer. The mosquito had been discovered to be more than just an annoying nuisance: the protozoa transmitted by it was the cause of several different types of malaria, the most severe type capable of causing death within a matter of hours. Even the more benign varieties were responsible for repeated and unpleasant feverish attacks. The parasites invaded the liver and the bloodstream, causing red blood cells to burst and, in chronic cases, causing enlargement of the liver and spleen.

When Kipling declaimed: 'The female of the species is more deadly than the male', he sure spoke a mouthful, to employ an American term. As with the human population in Africa, it was the role of the female mosquito to carry the nasties. It was the female mosquito alone who transmitted the disease. The male, in fact, is a harmless little chappie who lives solely on nectar; the female has to drink blood to feed her eggs.

Nor is the spreading of malaria the only trick in the female mosquito's repertoire. Yellow fever, producing jaundice and ending very rapidly in liver and heart failure, is also transmitted by her. So too is filariasis. Filariasis is caused by a larval worm entering the human body in the saliva of a bloodsucking mosquito, where it will dwell practically forever in the lymph and the blood vessels, joyriding through the body via the bloodstream whenever the fancy takes it. It can grow to a handsome 6 centimetres long and is the cause of craw-craw, a horrible pustulent itch of the inner thighs, and elephantiasis, massive swellings of the legs and genitals for which there is no known cure. Blackwater fever, a singularly unpleasant complication of malaria, causes widespread destruction of the red blood cells. (Blood pigments in the urine stain it a very dark brown, hence the name.) The death rate from this unpleasant malady was very high in the old days.

There were plenty of other unpleasant ailments, too, not necessarily connected with the mosquito. Wading across even the cleanest-looking rivers and streams could be fraught with hazard. Water-snails abound in tropical Africa, and they harbour the larvae of the parasitic bilharziasis. The microscopic larvae enter through the bodily orifices, and even the pores of the skin, setting up home in the blood vessels of the intestine and the bladder, causing anaemia, dysentery and – eventually and painfully – death. No water was ever considered safe to drink unless boiled and filtered, for the infamous guinea-worm, carried by water-fleas, was endemic. When swallowed by the human host, the guinea-worm burrows into the body tissues and lives happily inside the human frame for anything up to fifteen months, growing longer by the day. At the end of this time the female bores her way out to the skin surface (generally on the leg), where a blister forms and bursts, millions of microscopic larvae being released in the watery fluid. The female's head emerges briefly and this is the point at which she must be ensnared before she vanishes back to her cosy little nest inside. The bush African's method of achieving this – which I have often seen in practice – is to wind the threadlike worm around a bamboo splint a little bit at a time each day as it is forced to emerge further and further out of the flesh until, at last, the whole worm is carefully extracted. As the worm can reach a length of 150 centimetres (or 5 feet), it takes time and patience. There is an African belief that inadvertently snapping the worm's upper part will mean that the section inside the body will grow a new head and create further mischief. Whether there is any truth in this, one thing is for sure: guinea-worm infestation is singularly painful and unpleasant, and terrible ulcers form as a result of it.

Sweat-flies were a constant irritation to anyone living in the forest close to water. These tiny insects seem, at first, to be nothing more than a nuisance, for they do not bite at all but hover constantly around the eyes and ears and nose. However, they are now thought to be the source of yaws, a rather horrid tropical disease once thought to be of venereal nature – indeed, it cannot be distinguished morphologically from syphilis. Skin lesions are followed by a secondary stage in which ulcers develop all over the body, and then a third (and final) stage in which the bones are affected.

The little black hump-backed buffalo-flies cause river blindness, and clouds of tsetse flies still haunt the inland waterways, bringing with them the fatal sleeping sickness. In clearings and in villages, where I often saw the little black-and-white native cows grazing, the tombo-fly was a constant pest. The tombo-fly – a type of botfly – lays eggs around the scalp and neck as one sleeps. The larvae hatch under the skin, producing very painful boil-like swellings, under which the devloping larvae can actually be heard scraping away between cranium and scalp. When the 'boil' is 'ripe', it should be squeezed, and the large white wriggling maggots will erupt gruesomely to the surface where they may be despatched at leisure.

In my time, when one added to this litany of horrors the better-known ones such as cholera, smallpox and snakebite – some of the world's most lethal snakes are to be found in the rainforests of West and Central Africa – it could be understood why most sane people felt that only those imbued with a death-wish would want to have anything to do with working in the forests of the White Man's Grave, even in the 20th century when prophylactic drugs became much more sophisticated and effective.

The climate didn't help, either. The constant mugginess, the ever-lasting hot, hot, HOT, steaming humidity that drained the strength and the willpower and the very soul out of one by day did not ease with the coming of darkness. If anything – apart from a brief and blessed period around December when the harmattan mists from the north settled over the land to cool it down somewhat – the discomfort increased in the tropical night. In those pre-air conditioning days sheets became soggy within seconds of laying one's body down on the bed. Fans and punkahs were of little use; they simply shunted the hot air sullenly around the bedroom. As if this discomfort were not enough, every tiny recess of one's mind became gradually filled with the ceaseless churring of the cicadas out there in the black night. It would begin as a gentle and quite soothing sound, and then gradually evolve into a staccato thrumming of such aerodynamic intensity that it seemed as though every cicada in Africa had crowded itself into the bedroom and was doing its damnedest to ensure what little sanity the sweltering victim had managed to retain would be irrevocably shattered long before the African sun had risen over the treetops to banish the demons of the night.

As might have been expected, the brooding forests were rife with juju practices of the most disagreeable kinds. Sinister 'societies' abounded, most of them – such as the snake and leopard societies – being of a zoomorphic nature. Torture and ritual cannibalism were the order of the day in many parts of the rainforests. God Himself must have wondered why any nation should have wanted to go to war over such forbidding territory where it bucketed rain for half the year and everything that moved bit you or ate you. But fight over it they did, those big and powerful nations of the day. There were many fierce skirmishes involving France and Britain and Germany about the right to govern at least a portion of the lands bordering the Gulf of Guinea. Most of those skirmishes took place from the relative safety of gunboats firing their salvoes over coastal waters and the larger rivers, such as the Niger, and woe betide any of the African tribes who tried to join in the fun. 'Whatever happens we have got the Maxim gun and they have not,' as the poet Hilaire Belloc was later to observe.

Some of these spats could be quite bloody, but others – especially when viewed from the healing distance of a century or so – had a certain macabre humour about them. A French detachment, camped on a bend of the Sanagha River in south-eastern Cameroon during the Great War, had been celebrating their commander's birthday in suitably Gallic style with flagons of wine and brandy which their porters had been forced to carry through the forest, all the way from distant Yaounde in anticipation of the great event. Knowing that the nearest German troops were – according to their normally reliable bush spies – at least a couple of day's march away, they slept the sleep of the truly intoxicated after the party. During the night a fisherman arrived with the news that a heavily armed German gunboat was steaming up the river and heading their way. The French commander, tetchy on being wakened, knew that the move was quite impossible. He was brusque: 'Je m'en fou!' he retorted, with an irritable indifference he was soon to regret. ('I don't give a fuck!') The French were slaughtered to a man. To this day, the village that grew up around the site is known as 'Je m'en fou' and a plaque commemorates the spot where the incident took place.

Even in those times of periodic hostility there was a certain amount of trade between Africa and the outside, sporadic though it undoubtedly was. At irregular intervals between all these shenanigans, small consignments of this and that were shipped out for foreign shores, bound mainly for England and Germany. Most of the shipments were in the form of palm oil, coffee beans, rubber, piassava (palm fibre for making ropes) and beeswax. Along the coastal regions business was also quite brisk in gold, ivory and animal pelts, while from the savannahs and orchard scrub to the north of the great forests came solidified slabs of shea-butter (for the making of chocolate cream and margarine), and the pigment known as Indian yellow (made, incredibly, from the urine of camels).

Small consignments of camwood and ebony found their way to the Liverpool market, but these were, for the most part, regarded as little more than curiosities. Occasionally some entrepreneur with a sadistic sense of humour would slip into these timber parcels a few logs of some species hitherto known only to God, and these would inevitably end up on some unsuspecting factory owner's saw-bench, to the detriment of the saw-teeth and the sawmiller's blood-pressure. *Parinari excelsa* (euphemistically named 'African green-heart') and *Oldfieldia africana* (even more euphemistically labelled 'African oak') were two such. Both were truly spectacular to look at as growing trees, being straight and tall and cylindrical, a sawmiller's dream on the surface. They were, in addition, plentiful on the Coast. Unfortunately, once the saw bit under the log surface the dream turned to a nightmare, for the wood cells of each were full of silica and the timbers were of the consistency of wrought iron. In fact, so lasting was the impression created by those early samples that even today there are sawmillers who will turn purple at the very mention of any kind of timber emanating from Africa.

One of the more interesting of those early samples was recorded by Harold Unwin (in *West African Forests and Forestry*, 1920) as having been sold as 'a species of oak' on the Liverpool market in 1906 at one shilling and ninepence per cubic foot. This proved to be *Erythrophleum ivorense*, one of the first – and more common – species to be encountered just to the north of the coastal mangrove swamps. Predictably, it proved far too hard for the saws of that era (although today is is a popular flooring timber) and, like others of its ilk, it was consigned to the gradually mounting scrapheap of African timbers. Those who handled it then could not possibly have known that this was the infamous sasswood, which, through the virulence of the poison contained within its bark, had been respons-ible for so many horrific deaths throughout Africa's violent past.

These early disasters should, by rights, have signalled the death knell for African woods in the European timber trade. But attitudes were about to change. Intriguing reports were filtering through from the few creditable whites who had, willy-nilly, opted to live out their lives in the African rainforests. The reports indicated that not all timbers out there were of such intractable density. Indeed, there were plenty which could be worked just as easily as any of the traditional European species, and these offered an even greater variety of colour, density and durability than could be found in all the forests of Europe. In addition, it was reported, something akin to the true mahoganies of the American continent could be found in abundance in certain parts of the vast African forests.

Small sawmills already existed out there by the beginning of the 20th century, primitive though they were. After all, new ports were in the process of construction all along 'The Coast', and traders needed lumber for their stores and dwelling houses, and missionaries required timber for their schools, churches and clinics. That estimable medical missionary, Dr Albert Schweitzer, was one who depended greatly upon the timber resources around him while he was working in the Ogouwe forests of French Equatorial Africa (now Gabon) at the beginning of the century. In his book *More from the Primeval Forest* he writes about a species called 'okoumé' as being one which grew in abundance in the vicinity of his hospital, and which was, in his own words, '. . . the only timber considered worth exporting . . .' Timber camps in his area not only supplied lumber for his hospital buildings but even then also squared logs for the export trade. In fact, 'okoumé, or *Aucomea klaineana*, – exported today under the trade name 'gaboon', and much in demand for plywood – bears only a superficial resemblance to the African mahoganies and has none of their strength properties.

Eventually the lowering war clouds in Europe sparked the African export trade into life. Just before the outbreak of the First World War, the Germans shipped 18,000 tons of logs home to the Fatherland from Cameroon. At about the same time, the British shipped 80,000 tons, also in log form, from Nigeria. Significantly, this latter consignment was exported in its entirety under the trade name of 'mahogany'. It was to be the beginning of the great West African timber boom and – although no one then could have foreseen it – it would mark the beginning of the end for the great West African rainforests, although that end was still a long way off.

Only a relatively modest proportion of those two consignments could truly be termed 'mahoganies'. A more appropriate label would perhaps have been 'redwoods', for most, while being of the obligatory reddish-brown hue, bore little resemblance to mahoganies in their working properties. Yet the British certainly had discovered a legitimate substitute for the American mahoganies, and it even turned out to be a very close relative of the latter. *Khaya ivorensis* – or 'lagoswood', as it came to be called after the port from which it was originally shipped – was the first of the genuine African mahoganies to appear in Europe. Not only did it grow in abundance along the banks of the numerous waterways linking Lagos to the interior forests of Ijebu, it had the added advantage in that it floated even in its green state. It also turned out to be a most beautiful timber, with all the favourable working qualities of its American cousin. The race was on in earnest.

In the beginning, it seemed more like a race between antediluvian steamrollers, so slow, so cautious and deliberate were the protagonists. But, as with the movement of steamrollers, once started, it was inexorable, unstoppable. In those early days, suitable waterways were all-important. The placid creeks of the Niger Delta proved ideal for rafting and the long, narrow rafts of logs were poled down to the coastal shipping points. Felling was by axe and crosscutting of the felled trees into logs was effected by great two-handed saws. The logs were hand-hauled over wooden rollers through the forest to the nearest waterways by gangs of contract labour. Mechanical jacks were used to help roll the heavier logs into the water and timber dogs were hammered into the log ends to hold in place the ropes which would keep the logs together in the water.

Yet if jacks and timber dogs were about the nearest to any form of mechanization the logging industry in West Africa approached in the years leading up to the outbreak of the Second World War, already the big boys were moving in. Unilever – in the guise of United Africa Company and African Timber and Plywood – already had vast logging concessions in Nigeria and the Gold Coast, and they were not out there for either the good of their own health or that of the environment. They were there for one purpose only, and that was to make money. Nor would they remain satisfied with the paltry returns to be had from the archaic operating methods of the past and those currently being employed by the smaller companies. They were about to mechanize logging in a big way as soon as hostilities ceased in Europe.

Mechanization was certainly to expand the horizons of the logging industry dramatically. Bulldozers smashed roads into hitherto inaccessible places and vast juggernauts were soon hurtling daily to distant shipping points with ever-greater loads of logs. No longer was it necessary that logging operations be concentrated within the vicinity of waterways; the only limit now to the activities of the logger along the coast of the Gulf of Guinea was the northern tree line. Like the great forests of Canada and the United States, this bonanza was for ever.

It was wishful thinking. The tree limit did not extend quite as far north as was originally thought. West African tree growth was contained within a band stretching from Sierra Leone to eastern Cameroon, and this band was divided into five relatively narrow strips. Working from the coastal regions to the northern savannahs, these strips consisted of:

1. Coastal mangrove swamp, containing stunted trees and scrub in perennial swamp conditions, and of no interest to the logger.
2. Evergreen rainforest, with a network of rivers running north to south and containing closed-canopy forest of very large trees of many different species.
3. Mixed deciduous forest, with much drier conditions, both climatically and on the ground and – consequently – much more of the open-canopy type of forest, containing both deciduous and evergreen trees of many different species, often of very large girths.
4. Fringing forest, linking the foregoing to the parkland forest in the north. This type of forest tended to follow stream-beds and

to occur in isolated pockets. Tree species, while often of commercially desired species, tended to be of much smaller bole lengths than in the wetter forests to the south.

5. Parkland forest, located between the savannah grasslands to the north and the deciduous forest zone to the south. Trees here were always stunted, gnarled and scattered, and of no interest whatsoever to the commercial logger.

Only the evergreen and the mixed deciduous zones were of any interest to the really big operators. Smaller companies took whatever was left, although fringing forest areas – free as they often were from colonial forestry restrictions – could occasionally prove quite lucrative to them.

It was, after all, the law of the jungle: the big predators dined on the big stuff, while the little fellows had to make do with the scraps. It was within the vast expanses of evergreen and mixed deciduous forests that the logging giants plied their trade. Small, isolated pockets of forest were just not worth the effort for them. In most of the afforested countries along the Coast a system of forest reserves had been created which should, in theory, have protected the bulk of the forests for perpetuity. Those reserves were areas marked out and permanently set aside for the production of 'timber and other forest produce'. A timber company would apply for the right to become a concessionaire within one and, if successful, would be granted – within strict guidelines – the sole operating rights within that area. No tree under 4 feet in girth could be felled, and the operator would generally only be allowed to fell a hundredth of the area of his concession per annum. Thus, the concessionaire holding 100 square miles would be allowed to fell only one square mile of his total forest area each year, so by the time the whole area had been worked out and the hundred-year cycle had lapsed, the trees which had had to be left at the beginning through immaturity would now be ready for felling. But one hundred years is a long time in the fast-changing world.

Contrary to popular modern myth, colonial forest departments were both fair and scrupulously honest. While strict in enforcing the rules, they could be very tough indeed on any logging company, expatriate or otherwise, that tried to step out of line. The change that came in Africa was Macmillan's oft-quoted 'Wind of Change'. It descended upon West Africa like a tornado. When it had blown itself out, every country along the Coast had become independent. Unfortunately, not all of those who suddenly found themselves elected to positions of high authority were able to handle the responsibilities that came with their eminence. With temptation all around them, there were plenty who lost no time in bending the rules. Logging companies, smaller and much less reputable than those that had operated within the law on the Coast before independence, suddenly found opportunities for the less scrupulous. Backhanders became the order of the day and suddenly there was a feeding frenzy of logging piranhas all along the shores of the Gulf of Guinea. It is a feeding frenzy that goes on today.

The opening of the mahogany trail was a slow and leisurely business. Man had time on his hands then. The axe was good enough for him. Speed, and the greed that comes with speed, had not yet become fashionable. Along the way, many strange species were tried out by the timber men, and some that bore no relation to the famed mahoganies were even given a grudging welcome. Many species, though, were found wanting and left for the forest African to use, as he had always done, to make his canoes, or else for their fruits which he could eat or from which he could extract cooking oils, flowers from which he could derive fragrant spices and unguents, resins which he could use for lighting fuel, and bark extracts which he could use to cure or kill, whichever way the fancy took him.

All this was in the era of the felling axe, and when the axe was banished forever to the museum, everything changed. All too often, after the loggers had laid waste a tract of forest with their chainsaws and heavy hauling machinery, nothing would be left, for the subsistence farmers would move in with their machetes and their extensive families. By the late 1970's a new breed of forest African had arisen, and this one had little time for the old methods. There were now roads – built by the loggers – into the most remote parts of the

14

hinterland and 'civilized' goods were easily obtainable in the village markets and bazaars, pre-packed and bottled and stamped 'Made in Lahore'. What was the point in working up a sweat trying to extract all that old-fashioned rubbish from trees when all one's worldly desires could be readily obtained by sending one's child down to the market for it? In villages surrounded by trees, from which hung the most delicious fruits, canned European peaches did a very brisk trade in the markets.

Of the 70,000 or so species of timber-producing trees worldwide, it is estimated that not more than 500 are of much commercial interest to the timber trade. The prestigious Timber Research and Development Association (TRADA) lists 86 of the latter as being exported from West and Central Africa. In my experience, at the end of my time out there in the early 1980's, only 20 of those species were being accepted by exporters with maximum enthusiasm, while another 40 species were being taken by them with degrees of enthusiasm ranging from only moderate to downright tepid. Not a lot, perhaps, when one looks at these bald statistics, but, as already pointed out, it is the *way* in which they are removed from the forest which has proved so fatal.

The mahogany trail has been a long one. Where once about half a dozen species found their way to Europe, and these only because they were 'mahoganies', now white woods and yellow woods and grey woods – in fact, timbers of virtually all hues and densities – are being taken with almost equal fervour. The end, as the street corner evangelists proclaim, is nigh. Once upon a time a dense swathe of rainforest stretched all the way from Sierra Leone to Cameroon. As I write this during the last two months of the 20th century, 80 per cent of that forest has gone. Former major timber producers such as Nigeria, Ghana and the Ivory Coast have lost 90 per cent of their original rainforest. Now all that remains are the once-great forests of Central Africa, in Gabon, Congo and Zaire, and these have been under sustained assault for a number of years now.

The irony of it all has been that the African politician, to whose ancestors those marvellous forests had belonged in the first instance, has been only too happy to pocket the thirty pieces of silver offered to him by the foreign loggers to ensure his own co-operation – and willing participation – in the rape of his country.

Perhaps this final betrayal is the saddest epitaph of all.

Chapter 2

The Water Babes

Botanical Name	–	*Mitragyna ciliata*
Trade Name	–	Abura
Other Names	–	Bahia (Ivory Coast)
		Subaha (Ghana)
		Elilom (Cameroon)
Distribution	–	Sierra Leone to Gabon
Timber	–	Very pale brown. Grain straight to interlocked. Fine, even texture, with occasional sycamore-like figuring. Soft and easy to work, with good nailing and screwing properties.
Commercial Uses	–	Interior joinery; cabinet making; laboratory tables; battery boxes.

WHILE THE COMMERCIAL logger's only interest in the salty mangrove swamps and lagoons that separated the West African interior from the outside world was as through channels for his logs to reach their shipping points, the freshwater swamps and river borders to the immediate north of those mangroves were of enormous value to him. There he would set up camp for his future operations, and that was where the rainforests – his reason for being on the Coast in the first place – began.

It was in those areas of freshwater swamp that he became acquainted with a tree that would eventually prove to be of great benefit to him, although this fact was not apparent immediately. He could, perhaps, have been excused this lack of foresight, for the pale, dun, lack-lustre wood had none of the attributes of the mahoganies, and the tree itself grew in conditions in which no self-respecting mahogany would ever be found, conditions that made its felling and extraction a messy and laborious business. For the abura tree was ever a lover of wet and muddy places.

Very few tree species will survive permanent flooding. They drown. Abura is no exception, but unlike most others, it must have its roots embedded in very wet soil conditions all year round. Its home is the swamp, the marsh and the river bank, and permanent sub-soil moisture is necessary to its survival.

Abura is a highly gregarious tree. Where you get one, you are liable to find dozens, and the number clustered together in any one place will generally be limited only by the available water supply.

By African rainforest standards it is not a large tree, but in really favourable conditions it can reach a height of around 30 metres and a bole diameter of a metre. Rarely do you find it with full buttresses: more often, it will be equipped with low, thick root spurs around its base. Its trunk is tall and straight and cylindrical, with a rather dingy beige bark, soft and thick and deeply grooved longitudinally. The crown is surprisingly small and compact, with just two or three thick, stunted, crooked branches covered in large (up to 30 centimetres long) oval-shaped leaves which are a sort of terre-verte underneath and apple-green above. The flowers are small, pretty and abundant, carpeting the ground and the water under the trees in the early months of each year with their sweetly fragrant, creamy-white blossoms. The seeds are tiny, with a wing on each end, and they are distributed far and wide from their capsules with the least puff of wind during the months of March and April.

From the axeman's point of view, this was one of the easiest trees in the whole of Africa's rainforests to fell. The bole was rarely of large diameter, the buttresses, if any, were slight, and the wood was soft. But for the exporters, used to the more durable mahoganies, it had a few grave disadvantages, and one of those was the fact that its timber was of a perishable nature. It was not until the second quarter of the 20th century, when the demand for softwoods increased in Europe, that its potential began to dawn upon them. Today, its logs and its lumber can be found awaiting shipment in every major port along the shores of the Gulf of Guinea.

Despite its softness when green and its proven lack of durability, abura has a surprising firmness when dry, with strength properties akin to those of the common European elm. It dries easily and well, and is then very stable. It is excellent for small mouldings, and its resistance to acids has made it a favourite over the years for such items as laboratory tables, battery boxes and vats. It has proved to be ideal for plywood, and even for decorative veneer where figuring is found to be particularly marked in a log. All in all, it has come to be accepted as one of the best general utility timbers ever to have come out of Africa.

It has, of course, long been used as a timber tree by the people of the swamp, although its non-durable nature meant that its uses outdoors were somewhat limited. Canoes would sometimes be made from it when there was no more durable timber to hand. Such canoes were light and horribly unstable, and they were never expected to last long, but the wood was so soft that it took little time to replace an old one which had rotted away. The timber was often used indoors for such things as roof rafters, tables and chairs where, away from the humidity and the climatic vagaries of the great outdoors, they could be expected to last for a reasonable length of time.

Abura is one tree species that will probably survive. Regeneration can be prolific on favourable sites. Great clumps spring up around the verges of swamps, often so dense that it is impossible to force one's way through them. Young stems usually have very large leaves, and these were extensively used by fishermen for thatching their huts. I have also seen them used for the same purpose by the pygmies of central Africa when they were building their own little beehive-shaped huts in the heart of the forest.

Among the recognized African timber species, there are none that are so dependent on the swamp as abura. There is, however, one other, even softer and less durable species, whose lifestyle centres around the wetter parts of the rainforest, and that is the emien tree.

Emien (*Alstonia boonei* and *A. congensis*) is a tall, slender tree, light green of bark and with thin high buttresses that spread snake-like in all directions from the bole. Log exporters hate it: it degrades rapidly from the moment it is felled and wastage is therefore high. The timber is a pale yellowish-white in colour, quite attractive to look at but extremely soft and light, and logs are vulnerable to attack by blue-staining fungal organisms and boring insects every minute of every day that they spend in forest landings. Another drawback is that the timber often appears riddled with unsightly latex canals – slit-like holes about six millimetres across which are very visible on planed surfaces. Occasional shipments of logs are made from the Coast, however, (mainly from Cameroon, where it grows in abundance) for nowadays it has created a small niche for itself in the European market in the form of core plywood, crating material and rough interior carpentry.

This tree was often felled by the forest people in some areas. The softness of its timber and the ease with which it could be carved appealed to the village carpenter. His customers rarely worried about such trifling defects as blue stain and latex holes when all that they wanted was a couple of chairs for the house. The carpenter's requirements were of a much more basic nature than those of the white man. He made complete stools from solid blocks of emien wood, and he carved intricately designed masks for his witchdoctor from it. Over in the Yoruba lands of southern Nigeria he made the sweetly musical bush zither from the mellow softness of its wood. It was the timber on which budding bush carpenters practised their trade by making toys for the new generation and coffins for the old one.

Not all tribes felled it, though. Some hold it to be sacred, owing to the fact that during the dry months the leaves appeared to 'weep' constantly (because of heavy transpiration), giving a regular shower bath to anyone standing under them on the driest of days.

Many medicinal properties were attributed to the leaves, the bark and the fragrant flowers of the tree. Emien is related to the wild rubber tree (*Funtumia elastica*), and, when the bark is cut or bruised, it exudes a similar type of white latex. This was used in a number of native medicine preparations, including the treatment of malaria and snakebite.

Fortunately, even in the unlikely event that the demand for emien as an exportable timber will escalate dramatically in the foreseeable future, it is not going to be the logging men who will cause its demise. Such is its proliferation that emien would be one of the more difficult species to eradicate completely. Its seeds are disgorged in billions each season by the parent tree, and dendrologists have estimated there to be about one thousand of these to the ounce, so tiny are they. They are sent on their way by nature's 'parachute system', like thistledown, and in the early part of each year when the rains have gone they can be seen drifting in grey clouds through the forests. They are very fecund seeds, too. Within a few short months of their settling on the ground, most have become well-developed seedlings.

Of West Africa's recognized timber species, abura and emien are the two to which to title 'water babes' most fittingly applies. All trees need water to one degree or another, but few to the extent that those two species do. But there are others – perhaps not recognized by the outside world as timber species but nevertheless of enormous importance to the people who have to live in those once-great forests – that are dependant on the proximity of large amounts of water throughout the year. For example, the black gum (*Haplormosia monophylla*), which is found all along the Gulf of Guinea, never grows to much more than a small tree or shrub on the banks of a creek or an inland lagoon. The timber is beautiful, and it is often used to make furniture for chiefs and dignitaries and for ceremonial occasions. It has alternating dark and light brown stripes, and it takes a very high polish in its natural state. It is very hard and heavy, but surprisingly easy to work with hand tools.

Often protected by the forest people, the Guinea-pepper (*Xylopia guineensis*) is a common tree found on the banks of many creeks and rivers. Small and rather skinny, with untidy greyish bark that nevertheless reflects with a curious silvery sheen in the sunlight, it is most noticeable because of its strange looking fruit, black pods which project like bunches of fingers from central stalks on the branchlets. Highly aromatic, they are used in native medicine in numerous ways. They impart a most pleasant and peppery flavour to stews. I have seen them on sale in markets in southern Nigeria and Cameroon. The timber is light and strong, with a high degree of elasticity, and it is much used for paddles and rafting poles.

A strange and most beautiful tree of the swamps and waterways is the parkia (*Parkia bicolor*), named after Mungo Park, the noted Scottish surgeon-explorer. It is a tree I have always thought to be more worthy of display in some tropical garden centre than buried in the heart of the rainforests. It can, on occasion, be quite a large tree, but its bole is always most gracefully malformed, either in a smoothly sinuous way or bent into some strange shape or other. It is of a low forking nature, with a huge, branchy crown. The bark is a flaky rufous-red, and the mature leaves are feathery and bright green, falling from the tree *en masse* immediately after the rains. The crown remains bare for only a very brief period before the shiny new bronze-coloured leaves appear. The flowerheads, which arrive soon afterwards, are large and very colourful. They are produced in great quantity between December and February on the ends of very long stalks, looking for all the world like artificial pink and red lightbulb-shaped decorations hanging from an outdoor tree during the Festive Season in England.

At this time of the year, especially when the leaves are in their various stages of development, the crown can be very picturesque – a glorious patchwork of bright green and shiny bronze and vivid pinks and reds. From February onward, it can be just as striking, for now the fruits begin to appear in the form of orange-coloured bean pods, very similar in shape to those of string beans, only much longer, and these turn a deep purple as they ripen. The flowerheads are eaten by monkeys and the juicy pods by duikers and elephants.

In certain parts of West Africa, the parkia tree – though never gregarious anywhere – can be quite common, and part of the reason for this may be that it is rarely felled for its timber, which is of little value even to the forest native as it is soft and coarse grained and unpleasantly woolly to saw, and not in the least durable.

A curious tree of the river banks and swamps is the uapaca (*Uapaca guineensis*). Rarely a very large tree, it can grow to a height of 30 metres and a diameter of about a metre, but it is generally of much smaller size. Its base is a mass of stilt roots, with the actual bole commencing a metre or so above ground. In certain areas it can be quite gregarious. Its timber is hard, heavy and durable, reddish-brown in colour, and, although I have never personally known it to be exported except in the form of a few trial logs to the United States of America during the 1970's, I have read somewhere that logs of this species would sometimes be included among shipments of mahogany to Europe during the years immediately following the Great War. Now and again I have come across locals pitsawing logs of this species into plank form, and, among the coastal fishermen, its stilt roots would often be used as ribs and spars in dugout canoes. The fruits, something like warty gooseberries in appearance, are fragrant and very sweet.

Perhaps the most important function of the uapaca is the one for which nature so obviously intended it. Where severe flooding of rivers occurs on a regular basis, this species is the best anti-erosion device I have yet encountered. Its stilt roots have a very firm grip in Mother Earth, and this is a tree that is rarely washed away no matter how strong the current. Even when trees are knocked over by the force of the water, they never relinquish their hold; they simply lie there, roots anchored to the earth, until the situation returns to normal, when they immediately begin to sprout upward again to fill the gap created by their falling.

*　　*　　*　　*　　*

SWAMPS AND WATERWAYS in equatorial Africa are vibrant with life. Fish eagles patrol the skies above them by day and fishing owls by night. Antelopes like the long-legged sitatunga and the little hunchbacked chevrotain spend their lives in swamps and, when threatened, will dive without hesitation into the water, remaining submerged until the danger has passed. The black cobra, two and a half metres of truculent venom, is encountered on occasion, for he is a strong swimmer and appears to be fond of fish. The river jack, or rhinoceros viper as he is often called, will also be found on patrol in the vicinity of swamps. While not nearly as long or as agile as the black cobra, he is very much more cranky and he is absolutely lethal. The African python is, of course, celebrated in fable and in fact for his love of water. Pythons are not at all venomous and they are generally of a fairly placid nature, though a close encounter with one of those large serpents is usually worthy of a diary note. While wading through a shallow swamp on a dark night in Liberia I trod on a very large python, and it is a memory I shall probably carry with me to my grave. Another specimen, shot during the hours of daylight in a deep swamp, measured just over seven metres when I applied the tape to it several hours later after its contractions had ceased.

Oddly enough, crocodiles were creatures I rarely encountered in my travels, except in the vicinity of the Niger River. In certain areas, however, and particularly in parts of Liberia, the rare African dwarf crocodile used to be a lot less rare than supposed. This is a totally inoffensive creature, never much more than two metres in length, and it is very shy. It inhabits the more dense parts of the rainforests, sticking to swamps and small slow-moving streams and avoiding main watercourses. I encountered a number of them quite by chance in an area of abura swamp in eastern Liberia over the course of a couple of months. They are hunted mercilessly by humans, for their flesh is much prized. The 'handbag trade' is perhaps no longer what it was, but, with the combination of this type of relentless persecution and the inexorable erosion of its rainforest habitat, this is one more creature that seems doomed to extinction in the wild in our time.

An equally interesting – and equally shy – animal occasionally encountered in the swamp forests was the pygmy hippopotamus. Not much more than half the size of its better known cousin, the pygmy hippo is completely dependant on the rainforest. It is the original loner; it avoids the company of other hippos except at mating time, and flees for cover the moment it suspects the arrival of human beings. Unfortunately, this is another creature whose flesh is much sought by man, and like the dwarf crocodile, it is unlikely to have much of a future in the wild. One of the most pathetic sights I have ever seen was a fully grown pygmy hippo, each of its four feet caught in large steel traps, standing patiently by the side of a stream, just waiting to be butchered. Its feet were obviously mangled beyond repair by the terrible jaws of the traps, and I put it out of its misery with my rifle before the villagers who had set the traps could get to work on it with their machetes.

*   *   *   *   *

THE WATERWAYS OF the delta regions are placid places. They are my first real memories of Africa. I remember sitting in a canoe in the middle of a wide and sluggish creek in Nigeria, watching the Ijaws as they slowly guided their long and narrow rafts of logs to their distant destinations on the estuaries, listening to the spasmodic, high-pitched bursts of song which they emitted with each thrust of their poles down into the ooze of the creek bottom. This day had been my introduction to those most marvellous of watermen. This day was also to be my introduction to the bird known as the lily-trotter, and I was equally fascinated.

The lily-trotter is one species that – like the abura and the emien – will surely survive the reign of man on earth, and for much the same reasons. There will always be water in West Africa, and wherever there is water, there will be found the lily-trotter. It, too, is a highly fecund species, especially the female, for it is the male who is left to do the nest building, the incubating of the eggs and the rearing of the chicks, leaving her to mate with as many suitors as she chooses.

About the size of a moorhen and with the same sort of deliberate gait when on the prowl for food, the lily-trotter (or jacana, as it is often called) is the original water babe. It is beautiful. Its plumage is a rich chestnut-brown on body and wings, with black tail feathers and a chest of the most vivid gold. Its throat is a pristine white, and there is a jet-black stripe that runs from the back of its beak to cover its eyes and the back of its neck. Its head is the brightest light blue you ever saw in your life.

I stop paddling for a moment or two to watch him, for a 'him' this lily-trotter had to be, such is the resplendent nature of his costume. He stalks elegantly over the lily pads on his quaintly elongated thin claws, flipping over the occasional pad to check what morsel of food may be clinging to the underside. Now and again he stops, one leg upraised, cocking his head to one side to look at me, quite unafraid, even though my canoe is no more than a couple of metres from him. Suddenly, I become aware that there appears to be a pair of feet hanging down from under his wing as he walks by me and I think at first I am seeing things. I sit still and watch as he moves casually away from me, picking nonchalantly at the lily pads as he goes. Then, in the blink of an eye, a tiny chick drops down from under the wing and on to the lily pad. A second later, and from the other wing, another little chick pops out. They scurry after their parent over the lily pads, sometimes falling overboard, only to scramble back up with much splashing and frantic scrabbling of their sharp little claws. Within minutes, they and their parent are lost from sight among the reeds and the thickets of young abura by the waterside.

The lily pads bob gently on the water surface and their waxy white blossoms glow in the morning sunshine as I paddle my canoe back round the bend towards the Ijaw village.

Chapter 3

Liberia's Finest

Botanical Name   –   *Tetraberlinia tubmaniana*

Trade Name   –   Tet

Other Name   –   Ho (Liberia)

Distribution   –   Liberia's Western Province

Timber   –   Hazel-brown in young trees; coppery-brown in mature trees. Lustrous. Care must be taken in drying owing to checking tendency. Excellent strength properties. High elasticity. Takes polish well and works easily with all tools.

Commercial Uses   –   Veneer; general carpentry; furniture.

IN GROWTH HABIT, density and general appearance, a large stand of pure *Tetraberlinia* is probably the nearest a West African rainforest will ever get to the structure of a mature and natural coniferous forest. The perpetual gloom under a dense, green, locked canopy of other species of forest giants within the rainforests tends to inhibit growth under them, leaving only the most persistent of thorny vines and shrubs to fight for survival wherever the occasional shaft of sunshine does manage to penetrate the ceiling of foliage far above. In pure stands of *Tetraberlinia* one will find all sorts of age groupings and different storeys of saplings and trees, beginning at ground level with the abundant regeneration to be found among the D-storey agglomeration of vines and small shrubs of other species, through the C- and B-storeys of medium-sized tet trees intermingled with the trunks of mature parent trees. With tet, too, one will find spiky little dead branchlets and twigs protruding here and there from the main stems, particularly on their upper parts, a feature more typical of coniferous forests than of the rainforests of West Africa.

Looking at a stand of *Tetraberlinia* from a distance, there is, indeed, a sort of Christmassy look about it as a whole not normally associated with tropical rainforests. At first glance, it gives one the feeling that here is a stand of trees more properly belonging to the Boreal regions of the north. (Curiously enough, the timber itself has been utilized locally in Liberia under the misnomer of 'African Pine', although this species has absolutely no connection with pine or any other coniferous species.) There is, too, an almost fragile look about the tree that one does not associate with many other species of tropical hardwood, a look enhanced by the nature of its slight ascending branches, the openness of its crown and the smallness of its leaflets. A canopy of pure *Tetraberlinia* is no dense green blanket through which no sunlight can penetrate. On the contrary, sunlight percolates readily through the foliage, for on closer inspection it will be seen that the leaves and leaflets of tet are quite similar in appearance to those of the European ash. As is the case with ash, this gives the crown that lack of density so vital to the well-being of any regeneration growing underneath.

It is, by West Arican standards, only a medium-sized tree, scaling no more than 40 metres tall by a metre in diameter. It never has buttresses, but large mature trees may have heavy root swellings.

In another chapter of this book I have referred to a certain species as being the Mike Tyson of the tree world. That being so, tet would qualify as the super-model in my book. Everything about this species smacks of femininity, late 1990's-style. The bole is straight and cylindrical and willowy, and the greyish-green bark of young trees is smooth and unblemished. Only in old trees does the bark become rough, with corky excrescences. It is evergreen, flowering at the beginning of the rain season in May and fruiting at the height of the dry season in December. The tiny, velvety, rust-coloured flowers hang thick on the twigs and are sweetly fragrant, and the flat woody pods – about 10 centimetres long by 4 centimetres wide – expel their contents of two to three disc-shaped, amber seeds during the heat of the day with a pleasant, softly-crackling sound, the two valves of the pod twisting daintily round and round in the shape of a screw as they do so.

I have only ever come across *Tetraberlinia tubmaniana* in Liberia, and only in the south-western half of that country. However, at least one authority suggests that there may be the odd pocket of it in Sierra Leone, and this seems highly likely. It is strictly a tree of the wet evergreen forests bordering the coastline and it will be found only where there is a prolonged rain season. But, while it will form large stands in bottom lands, it cannot tolerate swampy conditions or land that is permanently or periodically inundated.

Coastal storms can create minor havoc in *Tetraberlinia* stands for, like the spruce forests of northern climes, tree density is usually so high that when one tree falls a hundred will fall along with it. This creates a bonanza of land and timber for the entrepreneurial subsistence farmers and pitsawyers. Nothing is wasted: locals use the timber for carpentry, building purposes, and for sale to the many thriving industries in coastal towns such as Greenville, Buchanan and Monrovia. Even small unmarketable sizes are sold as firewood or converted into charcoal.

In the 1970's, mainly through the promotional activities of a large American company that set up shop in the country, tet found a niche is the overseas markets. While the bulk of it was exported to the U.S.A. in log form, a steady trickle filtered through to a largely unenthusiastic European market. It has, however, slowly proven its worth as a good quality timber for most interior uses. It is moderately hard but easy to work, and its grain pattern is attractive, although without any of the traditional figuring of the West African mahoganies. It appeals to the plywood industry for it peels well, and the logs are nearly always of such modest girths as to be easily handled. From my own fairly extensive experience with this species, it is not very durable. If logs are left uncovered or untreated for a few days in the open, they are very susceptible to sun-cracking and pinworm attack. I have also found that trees from certain areas tended to be prone to spiral grain, while trees from adjacent areas would be quite free from this annoying defect. In cases of severe spiral grain a tree would, given a week or so in a sun-baked landing with minimal cover, unravel suddenly and in most dramatic fashion, corkscrew-like, with a crack like a rifle shot, leaving nothing but a torn and twisted, completely useless length of wood fibre where, a split second before, there had been a hale and hearty bole. It paid the logger operating in suspect areas to get rid of his logs quickly before they were sussed out, and equally wise was the potential customer who gave each log a thorough examination before finally accepting logs from such dubious sources.

Because of their dense nature, stands of *Tetraberlinia tubmaniana* are not places in which one would expect to find other species growing readily, except perhaps in the case of two species. The ubiquitous mahtu tree (*Calpocalyx aubrevillea*), one of the more common species in Liberia's evergreen forests, will be found either scattered freely around the fringes of tet stands or in little pockets of its own along the banks of streams in close proximity to tet.

The mahtu tree is a smallish tree, rarely exceeding 25 metres in height and a metre in diameter. The bole is rarely straight and it forks low. The base of the tree has thin, wide-spreading buttresses and the bark on the bole is smooth and of a distinctive greyish-white hue. Like tet, it is a leguminous tree, with thick, extremely hard woody pods about 30 centimetres long which, when ripe, explode open to fire out three large purple seeds. The characteristically large valves of the fruit pod are shed from the tree soon after, stubbornly refusing to decay in an unyielding ligneous carpet under the tree for many moons to come, thus making this tree one of the easiest species in all of Africa to identify.

During my earlier years in those forests, some tribes still followed the ancient practice of setting fire to mahtu timber in order to obtain 'country salt' by leaching it from the ashes. However, this was a practice in decline even then, and I never knew of any other use being made of this species. I found the timber to be quite useless, and even the native of the forest – who could normally find a use for just about anything – treated the tree with some disdain once its days as a source of country salt were over. The timber is very soft and light and subject to instant attack by every known fungus and wood-boring insect from the moment of felling. A further draw-back, which I discovered through experiments carried out in a Liberian sawmill, was that the timber began to warp and twist and buckle every which way from the moment it was sawn, regardless of the dimensions into which it had been rendered or the care taken with it in drying.

This is one species that will survive the logger, for no one wants it. It will even, I suspect, survive the slash-and-burn farmer, for regeneration is prolific everywhere, and the kind of terrain sought by the farmer for growing his crops is equally favourable to the mahu tree. Indeed, the farmer's activities may well be beneficial to its development, for the mahtu tree is a lover of light, particularly in the early stages of its growth. It may, in the words of an old song, be 'Nobody's Child', but it is a survivor.

Didelotia idae – or to give it its marvellous local name, the woronggobonoh tree – is the other species that is often found in the vicinity of a tet forest. A much more handsome tree than the mahtu, the woronggobonoh is straight and cylindrical, attaining a height of anything up to 35 metres of straight bole and a diameter of 1.20

metres. Like tet, it lacks buttresses and has heavy root swellings, and its bark is of a pleasantly smooth, greyish-green hue, often prettily patched silvery-grey with lichens. The crown is small and dark green, and at the beginning of the dry season it sheds its old leaves and takes on the new with quite astonishing rapidity. At this time it is very conspicuous from the air as the new leaves are a shiny brilliant scarlet.

Unlike the mahtu, this is a tree which does find favour with the pitsawyer. Its timber, while having no particularly outstanding characteristics that would make it an instant hit with the export trade, is of a quite pleasant brownish hue, often with darker streaks running through it. It is easily sawn and can be worked with the crudest of hand tools. It is not very durable, however, and would probably only be suitable for general indoor carpentry.

Didelotia regeneration is prolific and, as it is less demanding than either tet or the mahtu (I have seen it growing on the rockiest of terrain), its long term prospects look good.

*   *   *   *   *

ANIMALS ABOUND IN Liberia's *Tetraberlinia* forests. Large-spotted genets glide in their sinuous and tippety-toe sort of movement through the rain-soaked woods. Their characteristic gait earned these strange civet-cats the evocative description of 'waltzing-trot' from poetic naturalists. As with most genets, this one is a night hunter. It sleeps by day in holes in trees or cracks in rocks, its soft creamy fur with large rust-red blotches giving it the perfect camouflage against intruders. Like its close relative the mongoose, it is the supreme hunter, being a superb climber and swimmer, and almost entirely carnivorous. It will eat absolutely anything, from beetles to birds and snakes, even rodents considerably larger than itself. It stalks its prey like a domestic cat and, as it pounces, the hairs on its bushy tail stand stiffly erect, making it look like a flying bottle-brush. As it lands on top of its prey and sinks its teeth in, it emits a loud and gruesome purring sound.

There are ten species of genet, one of them, the small-spotted or savannah genet, having actually been tamed and kept as a rat catcher in Egyptian households during the earlier Pharaonic dynasties. It was eventually thrown out by disenchanted housewives and replaced by the domestic cat, not because it was any less efficient at its duties than the cat – it was, if anything, much more so – but because of its deplorable tendency to eject the most evil-smelling anal fluid whenever and wherever the fancy took it.

A close relative of the genet, also commonly to be found in the wetter Liberian forests, is the African civet. This animal has none of the graceful sinuosity of the genet, however. Its gait is a sort of a comical waddling run, rather like that of an obese holidaymaker on a Blackpool beach hurrying down to the sea before the weather turns nasty. It is about the size of a sheepdog, rather squat and cumbersome in appearance, with a long bushy tail and a short powerful neck. It is rough-coated, the upper side being dark grey and the underside black. Its flanks are grey, with a vivid regular pattern of black stripes and blotches. The tail is grey, too, with wide black rings and a black tip.

Civets are nocturnal, and anyone driving along logging roads in the heart of the Liberian forests at night will quite commonly come across them, caught in the glare of the headlights.

Unlike the genet, the civet is strictly terrestrial, only climbing trees in dire emergency. While the male's vocal sounds are usually restricted to the odd exasperated growl and the occasional HA-HA-HA throaty contact call, the female is very loquacious, especially when she is in heat. She seems to be in heat for most of the year, too, for her penetrating mewing, like that of the domestic cat, is one of the most common sounds of the Liberian forest.

The civet stinks. There is no other word for it. Body odour began with the civet. Apart from its strong, gorilla-like bodily pong, it ejects constantly and copiously – like the genet – an anal gland secretion, one which has traditionally been collected over the ages in Muslim parts of Africa for use as a basis for perfumes. God knows what they do with it to turn it into perfume, but it is certainly no perfume when it leaves the civet.

The African civet is formidable. There are few creatures that it fears, even humans, and it will protect its young bravely against any

33

foe. It will eat almost anything, from small birds to eggs, fruits, berries, nuts, vegetation, toads, reptiles and domestic poultry. But its favourite snack is probably the domestic cat, even being so bold on occasion as to emerge from the forest in darkness to snatch unwary moggies from verandahs as their unsuspecting owners sleep inside their houses.

Much more attractive in every way are the members of the squirrel family. They are numerous in Africa, with more species than you could shake a stick at. Common in southern Liberia is the giant forest squirrel, a creature of about the size and body length of a dachshund dog. Its tail is about the same length as its body.

The giant forest squirrel is not restricted to Liberia. Its range extends from Sierra Leone to Kenya, wherever there is forest. But it is very common in *Tetraberlinia* forest, mainly around clearings or forest fringes, or in the vicinity of farm enclaves. Although it will eat nuts or fruit or leaves or bark of favoured trees, and, on occasion, even a nestling or two, its favourite food is the fruit of the oil palm. To it, along with the various species of monkey, can undoubtedly go the credit for the wild oil palms one finds scattered throughout the rainforests.

The giant forest squirrel is a handsome chappie. Reddish-brown in colour on head and back, it has bright alert eyes and a greyish-white throat and belly, and its tail is a luxuriant masterpiece of wide sepia and chocolate rings.

It spends much of its time in the highest tiers of the forest, only on rare occasions coming down to the forest floor for fallen fruit. Its voice is the scolding, chattering sound common to most of the squirrel family the world over, but it is probably best known to those who live in the forest for the incredible power of its early morning 'wake-up' call, a far-reaching, booming KU-KU-KU-TEKONDERU . . . KU-KU-KU-TEKONDERU . . . that fairly reverberates through the trees. When one hears it for the first time, it sounds as though it just had to be made by some colossal jungle denizen hitherto unknown to science. For me, the sound is most evocative of this particular part of Africa, waking me in the tent as the first glimmer of light filters through the branches of mist-wreathed forest giants. The ventriloquial boom of the giant forest squirrel somewhere out there among the high tops is telling the world that it is time to be up and doing.

Probably the most curious members of the whole squirrel family in Africa, however, are the so-called flying squirrels. Depending on species, they can range from mouse-size to cat-size. They are usually squirrel-like in appearance, but they are equipped with a bat-like membrane which they can spread at will between their arms and their legs, and which they use for gliding purposes. Despite their name, they can only glide, and are incapable of flight in the manner of birds. Most are equipped with very sharp horny spurs under the tail root as an aid to climbing trees.

The most grandly named of this genus is without doubt Lord Derby's flying squirrel. It is also one of the most colourful, with its silvery-grey head and throat and dark-red back. The gliding membrane is very dark red, with black hairs sprinkled throughout the red. Its belly is white and its tail is black. Regrettably, both its body odour and its voice are rather a let-down to its otherwise aristocratic image: it has a most potent monkey-smell and its voice is a prissy, squeaky, bat-like twittering.

Like most flying squirrels, Lord Derby's is nocturnal, hanging on the inside of its tree hole during day-long sleep. By night, it feeds on fruits, flowers, nuts and leaves.

It is a forest dweller by inclination, but where there is sufficient food to attract its attention it is not averse to taking up residence in burned out trees in forest clearings. Wherever it happens to find itself, however, its lifestyle never varies. At dusk, it emerges from its hole and scuttles rapidly up the tree in most ungainly fashion, making vigorous use of its sharp claws and tail spurs until it reaches a satisfactory altitude, at which point it launches itself into space like a hang-glider. It is remarkably graceful in flight and it can glide for up to 300 metres, even occasionally showing off its skills by executing the most elegant, wheeling, right-hand turns while in full flight. It seldom glides down to ground level, presumably because it is well aware of its extreme vulnerability, for it can only move there in laborious hops, like an arthritic rabbit.

All the squirrel family are considered delicacies in the rainforest. I confess to having eaten several varieties and found most to be quite palatable – though certainly not Lord Derby's flying squirrel, whose flesh was dark and strong, with the aura of elderly anthropoid hanging around it even after prolonged cooking.

Apart from the genet and the civet, the *Tetraberlinia* forests of Liberia were home to another hunter, the greatest of all African rainforest predators – the leopard. The proliferation of game and the dense undergrowth afforded by the more open nature of the tet canopy gave ideal cover for the leopard's ambushing style of hunting. A few leopards were shot by local hunters during my time in that area, but generally they were left well alone as they had a quite undeserved reputation for ferocity. However, there was one particular animal whose activities were to give me a considerable headache.

I had found myself – most reluctantly and briefly – in charge of a multi-million dollar American logging company. A high perimeter fence had been erected around the compound where the expatriate families lived, but the ever-resourceful civet population in the surrounding forests had dug a series of large holes under it from time to time in order to have access to the cats and poultry within. The fence had to be checked regularly to ensure that these holes were filled in, and periodically I would stroll round it myself to ensure that the checkers of the fence were doing the job they were paid to do. On one of those trips I came across the tracks of a very large male leopard which had obviously taken to prowling around the fence on a nightly basis, and it was with some consternation I noted that he had made use of one of the holes on the previous night, presumably in order to check whether there was any possibility of an easy snack inside. I hastened to my office and dictated a notice:

Mothers wishing to retain their progeny on strength would be well advised to refrain from allowing them to stray beyond the bounds of the expatriate compound. A large male leopard has taken to patrolling the perimeter fence and, while there is no indication as yet that he is any fonder of American children than the writer of this notice, there is also no reason to assume that he may not be as prone to sudden gastronomic whims as the rest of us.

In the event, the only damage done was to my own reputation. My undiplomatically-worded missive was taken to be a gigantic slur upon the youth of the United States of America, and vituperations rained down on my head for months to come from outraged Americans from outposts as far removed as Tulsa, Oklahoma and Balikpapan, Borneo.

*   *   *   *   *

*T*ETRABERLINIA TUBMANIANA – THE name is significant. Not because of the *Tetraberlinia* part of it, which simply refers to the fact that tet had originally been placed within the genus '*Berlinia*' but had been switched to that of *Tetraberlinia* when botanists discovered the flowers to have only four sepals (Greek – '*tetra*', meaning 'four'), as distinct from the five sepals of the *Berlinia* flowers. Rather, the significance lies in the fact that this species of *Tetraberlinia* was named after the then President of Liberia, William V. S. Tubman, who, by his 'open door policy' for trade after the Second World War, opened the Liberian forests to commerce.

The original idea was laudable enough, for no country along that febrile coast needed the money more than Liberia after the war had ended. It also seemed harmless enough insofar as the country's timber resources were concerned, for the European timber trade – used as they were to the richness of the forests of Ivory Coast, Gold Coast and Nigeria – tended to regard Liberia as a bit of a joke. Few bothered to find out what its forests contained in those early days. Most certainly, no one bothered about the large stands of *Tetraberlinia* in the south of the country, virtually unknown as a species. But the 'open door policy' was significant, for it proved to be the thin end of the wedge. The great commercial vultures may not have bothered to land in those days but they were certainly flying overhead, scanning the land below for possible pickings in case their supplies began to dry up elsewhere.

It didn't take long. In the early 1970's log exporters, big and small, suddenly appeared on the Grain Coast, sniffing the hot humid air with a certain amount of disdain and apprehension. Along the coast in the direction of Cape Palmas a large American company moved in. With the ample co-operation of the then Tolbert administration, they commenced the construction of a massive and highly ambitious sawmill and plymill factory. God knows what they intended to put in it, for it would have taken more timber than Liberia could ever have provided to keep such a monster going. In any case, even while they were building it, they were flattening vast areas of their forest concessions and selling the product in log form to the highest bidders. Little heed was paid to minimum felling girths or indeed to conservation of any kind. The *Tetraberlinia* forests in particular suffered, for this was one species that just could not tolerate full exposure to the fierce glare of the tropical sun which became the inevitable result of this sort of irresponsible felling. Its bark cracked and exuded copious quantities of gum, a sure sign of an ailing tree. *Tetraberlinia tubmaniana* is a delicate species, and felling and silvicultural programmes involving it need to be implemented with care and knowledge of the species, considerations that were obviously far from the minds of those who sought only the 'quick-buck-and-get-out' policy of that sad decade.

Ironically, this is one species that might – just might – be the sole beneficiary of the savage tribal wars racking this unfortunate country at time of writing. Timber operations, along with just about every other form of business, have ceased completely throughout the land, with the result that whatever is left of the *Tetraberlinia* forests are at last getting a much-needed breather.

However, I fear that it is already too late. Too much damage has been inflicted. Liberia's finest tree has all but joined the dodo in man's inexorable march towards self-destruction.

Chapter 4

The Crooked Man of Sapo

Botanical Name   – *Heritiera utilis*

Trade Name   – Niangon

Other Names   – Wishmore (Liberia)
Ogoué (Ivory Coast)
Nyankom (Ghana)

Distribution   – Sierra Leone to Ghana and Cameroon to Gabon

Timber   – Nut-brown, with golden lustre. Interlocked grain, with coarse texture. Feels greasy. Fairly easy to convert with all tools. Nails, screws and glues well and takes good finish. Requires quite a lot of filler.

Commercial Uses – All types of carpentry, cabinet and furniture making; boat building.

Few species of tropical tree in the whole world were less likely to attract the timber barons of Europe than this one. When niangon first came to the notice of the dendrologists back around 1900, an age when size meant everything, this tree was a disgrace. Indeed, from the point of view of tree size and shape, the first niangon stands encountered by the the the early timber prospectors – just to the north of the mangrove swamp line in the Ivory Coast and Liberia – would not have looked out of place had they been discovered as part of an area of neglected woodland somewhere in southern England.

It is true to say, though, that swampy conditions could not be considered the ideal environment for optimum growth of this species. Niangon will certainly grow quite happily and in great abundance with their roots wallowing in water for a good part of the year, but on the drier slopes surrounding the swamps fewer trees will be found per hectare and their diameters will be much greater and bole shape far better. That much admitted, however, niangon will never be a tree to attain the splendour and size of any of the mahoganies, no matter how favourable the conditions in which it happens to be growing.

It is a strangely shaped tree. Wade through a swamp full of them in the mists of early morning and you will find yourself among scenery that would not have been out of place in one of the early Hammer horror films. Rest your back against a tree and look around you. Let your mind wander a little, and you will almost expect to see creatures from the Mesozoic era emerge from their twisted shadows to browse among their branches.

As most rainforest timber trees go, the niangon is neither a tall nor a bulky tree. It seldom grows to more than 35 metres in height, and it is rarely more than 90 centimetres in diameter. It is also quite unusual to find a bole that has any part of it straight and cylindrical for more than three metres. A further drawback from the logger's point of view is that the tree often begins to sprout branches at well below the 20 metres mark, leaving a less than desirable length of trunk from which to select quality logs.

The peculiarly sinuous shape of its trunk is often complemented by the incredible shapes its buttresses can assume, particularly in perpetually marshy conditions. These shapes are stranger and more variable than I have ever encountered on any other species. In dry conditions, the buttresses can generally be rather ordinary looking – thin, spreading plank buttresses. In wet conditions, they may be tall arch-shaped flanges reaching to well over four metres up the trunk, or they may be bizarre-looking shapes that are something between stilt roots and plank buttresses, or the tree may in fact be equipped with simple stilt roots. What adds to the air of confused unreality is the fact that the tallest buttresses often grow on the spindliest of trees and the most pronounced of stilt roots on trees growing on rocky hillsides far from the source of the nearest water.

Nothing can be accepted as the norm in the Lewis Carroll world of the niangon.

There is a strange surreal sort of beauty about this tree, which the weird contortions of both bole and buttresses only serve to emphasise. The bark is a warm autumnal brown colour, fibrous, and with the dead outer bark peeling off in long strips to reveal an inner layer of the most delicate pink. The bark of the buttresses is markedly different; it has none of this thick brown outer coat. There the bark is thin and hard and stippled with a macedoine of muted hues ranging from olive green through cream, yellow, grey, orange, blue and violet.

The crown is something of an eye-catcher, too, but in rather a different way. Niangon is from the same family as the cacao, and when you look at its crown you may see some vague similarities. It has rather a narrow crown, but there is none of the compact firmness about it seen in many of the tropical timber trees; it has more of the sort of looseness that you tend to find in European sweet chestnut trees.

As you might expect from such an odd natural structure, the tree bears two quite different types of leaf. On the upper surface of the crown, the leaves are single and simple, while on the underside of the crown and on suckers and saplings they are digitate, with five to seven leaflets arising finger-like from the same stalk. Leaves and leaflets are very variable in size, but generally they are anything up to 25 centimetres in length and 10 centimetres in width, glossy

41

green on the upper surface and a rich hazel hue underneath, so that as one looks up through the canopy while a breeze is stirring the foliage, causing the hazel and the green to shimmer against aquamarine glimpses of sky beyond, the effect can be quite breathtaking in its beauty.

The fruit is a golden-brown, single-winged seed, very much like a half section of that of sycamore or maple, but about twice the size of the latter. It is most edible, but although many things eat it, regeneration is prolific because such enormous quantities are produced annually by each tree, particularly during the frequent mast years.

When I first encountered niangon, in the coastal regions of the Sapo tribe of Liberia, I thought of it as primarily a swamp tree, but the further north one goes away from the coastal flats into the drier areas of the evergreen forest, the larger will be the tree sizes and the better the quality of timber from fewer trees. This is one species whose timber can compete on almost equal terms with the better-known African mahoganies. Indeed, in some aspects – such as in laboratory-controlled strength tests – it has proved itself to be superior to the latter. Admittedly, it is somewhat coarser and denser than most of the African mahoganies, but it can produce a most attractive figure when quarter-sawn, and, as it ages, it develops a warm reddish-brown hue that has an almost golden sheen.

Niangon has been the big success story of the timber industry during the latter part of the twentieth century. Everywhere one goes its timbers are to be seen, whether as part of a humble door or window frame in some inner city housing estate or in the more rarified atmosphere of an up-market London furniture shop.

At times it used to strike me as odd that the interior Africans appeared to make so little use of this species, but in the wetlands its form was so poor that pitsawing it into planks would have been difficult. In the north, where the better sizes and shapes prevailed, the trees were often so far from human habitation as to make felling and pitsawing them not worth the effort. Other species were much closer to home. There also appeared to be little use made of the tree for food or medicine. Its seeds were occasionally boiled and eaten, but that was about all. Neither was I able to find any particular tradition of juju associated with the tree, though such was the esoteric nature of the various societies within this country that there may well have been rituals connected with niangon to which I was not permitted access.

There were four species which I often found to be closely associated with niangon, particularly in the wetter parts of the rainforest. All four were used by the forest people in a variety of ways long before the arrival of the European – and were still being used in those ways even during my time there. Abura (*Mitragyna ciliata*), nowadays a well known timber species on the export market, has already been discussed in an earlier chapter. The genie tree (*Loesenera kalantha*) is quite unlike the niangon in that it is tall and straight and elegant. Its timber is tough and strong, but it has so far escaped the attentions of the professional logger because its slender diameter renders it of little interest to the overseas markets. The genie tree was extremely important in juju. Before the arrival of organized central government, there were parts of West Africa in which the death penalty would be invoked if anyone even *damaged* this tree, such was its significance in witchcraft. It was revered by all the tribal people, but most of all by the local witchdoctor for its reputed power to 'top up' the magical properties of his charms and amulets when their effectiveness had begun to wane.

The spirit of the tree could be consulted by any tribesman on any matter that happened to be troubling him at the time, and the way in which the spirit of the tree responded – through the falling of a seed pod, a flower, a leaf, or by the way in which a slice of bark slashed off the bole would fall to the ground – would be given an appropriate interpretation by the witchdoctor, who had to be paid for each consultation. His fee varied quite considerably according to the magnitude of the problem. Thus, a few dollars would help you dispose of an argumentative wife instantly and for ever, but a very important matter, such as curing your sick cow, would cost you considerably more. Even in my day, witchdoctors were among the most affluent people I knew.

Apomé (*Cynometra ananta*), is another niangon associate. This species has a generic name that means, almost literally, 'genitals of a bitch', (Greek – '*kunos*': dog, and '*metra*': womb, uterus), because that is, reputedly, what the fruit of one of the Malaysian species resembles.

I suspect that the gentlemen of science must have been feeling a trifle liverish when they tagged apomé with such an appalling name, for it is, in fact, a handsome tree. Tall and heavily branched, with a russet-hued bark, it flourishes along river banks and on slopes surrounding swampland, and its timber is hard, heavy and durable. It has never made much of an impact on the export market, chiefly because it is extremely difficult to work with all but the most sophisticated of machine tools, and it is virtually impossible to drive nails into the wood or glue it. Various government departments in its lands of origin use it for heavy construction work such as bridge beams, wharf piling and railway sleepers, but the timber's impossibly hard and heavy nature never brought much interest from the forest African. In witchcraft, however, its seeds, leaves and bark were used for many different purposes. One of the more intriguing of these was for the conveying of messages to distant friends. The leaves were ground to powder and blown from the hand to north, south, east or west, according to which point of the compass the friend happened to be staying, while the message was called out.

The fourth tree, faro (*Daniellia thurifera*), is a very large tree of the wetland forests with a perfectly cylindrical bole. It is also a singularly beautiful tree, especially when it has shed its leaves around the end of January, after which it produces new and vivid scarlet leaves, a very prominent feature of the swamp forests at this time of the year to anyone travelling by air along the coastline. This is one tree that has made it in the world of the log exporter, despite the fact that it is both soft and resinous, as it has become a popular substitute for spruce in the manufacture of such items as packing cases and core plywood. Liberians call it 'gum copal', and indeed a creamy coloured resin – later turning to dark amber – exudes slowly and copiously from it when tapped. At one time, it was exported to

Europe as 'gum copal', but it could never be produced in sufficient quantities to make it a viable proposition.

Still, in the heart of whatever forests there are left on the Coast, the locals tap its resin to this day. (The very best quality is taken from the rotted roots of long dead trees, where it will be found in huge solidified lumps.) An oil is made from both the tree seeds and the resin for use by the women as a body lotion and hair unguent. The oil is applied with tasteful perfection by those maidens of the forest; neither too much, nor too little. After their evening bath they will spend ages grooming themselves, rubbing themselves all over with the oil. It is an oil that imparts upon them a uniquely delicate and lovely fragrance that lingers even as they toil and sweat on their little patches of farm throughout the heat of the following day.

Although all these species can be found growing well away from obvious water supplies, it is on lands bordering the swamps and rivers of the Coast that I best remember them. That was always where they seemed most at home to me. Niangon could certainly prosper mightily on the driest of hillsides, but it did not seem to belong there.

Food was in abundance for herbivore, insectivore and carnivore alike in those niangon forests. All through the night the leopards stalked, feeding upon those whose diet was restricted to the more humble things in life, and one of the creatures on their very extensive menu was the pangolin.

This curious little animal – about 100 centimetres long, and most of that length taken up by tail – is the original living, walking, breathing tank. In the rainforests, only man and leopard threaten its existence, for they are the only creatures big enough and strong enough to prise it open when it curls itself into a tight ball with the sharp spines on the ends of its armour plating raised protectively against the enemy. It is covered in this armour plating, from the tip of its long snout to the end of its tail. It has no teeth at all, its diet consisting of soft-bodied insects, particularly termites. It shambles along on its front knuckles with the foreclaws tucked underneath to protect its precious digging equipment, its long and powerful claws.

Leopards love the pangolin, as do human beings, unfortunately. But it is not easily taken: a gland near its anus expels foul-smelling liquid guaranteed to repel all but the most determined of predators. This is another of the many rainforest species that I have, to my eternal regret, eaten on my travels, and I have to admit that it is quite delicious.

An even odder creature to be found prowling around the fringes of the niangon forest was the aardvark. About 200 centimetres long from nose to tail and weighing around 65 kilograms, this large creature, when encountered suddenly on a lonely forest trail at night, is like nothing else ever created by God. It is, without question, the strangest looking creature I have ever seen. The word 'aardvark', I am informed, is Afrikaans for 'earth pig', but this does not even begin to describe it. Although it lives in a hole in the ground all right, its body, while vaguely pig-like in shape, is yellowish-grey in colour and sparsely haired, with an enormously long and flexible snout and huge bat-like ears, giving it an appearance more like a cross between a pig and a kangaroo. It can even stand on its hind legs, balancing on its thick tail when on the lookout for danger. Its claws are so powerful that it can break through termite mounds too hard even for a man armed with a pickaxe to penetrate. Ants and termites are its favourite food, and it hoovers them up with a sticky tongue that measures an incredible 45 centimetres. Ants and termites are rarely in short supply in the African rainforest, but should the unthinkable happen and times get really hard, then the aardvark will quite happily settle for a diet of fruit.

It is a totally inoffensive creature, despite its appearance. Unfortunately for it, though, its flesh is very good to eat, and its three main predators – python, leopard and the inevitable man – take it whenever they can. Should it be cornered by any of these, however, it can give a fair account of itself, lashing out with its thick and powerful tail and hurling itself at its persecutor with all four feet slashing.

Strangely enough, the aardvark is not considered endangered at time of writing. Termites are on the increase in Africa, and ants will be around long after the human race has vanished, so its food supply is secure.

The porcupine was common, too, in this part of the world in my time. Predators had to be pretty desperate to tackle this customer, armed as it is with masses of 30-centimetre-long, needle-sharp quills. Although I have seen it on the prowl by day, it is basically a nocturnal creature. It eats roots, bulbs, fallen fruit, berries, and – on the very rare occasion – carrion. When threatened, it charges rapidly backwards, quills erect, and I know of no creature that will face up to a porcupine when it is in this mood. Its quills become detached at the slightest contact with an adversary's flesh, and once in, they stay in. In fact, because the quill head is covered in tiny barbs, each movement of its victim, no matter how slight, simply pulls the quill deeper into the flesh. A painfully protracted death from infection is the usual end result.

On one occasion I was shown a large dead python by a hunter who had found the body in the forest. It had rather foolishly attempted to swallow a porcupine, and eight quill points were sticking out through its body. The hunter's courteous invitation to share his python-and-porcupine casserole later that evening was declined by me on the pretext that I had a pressing engagement elsewhere. Maggots were noticeably heaving under the python's skin, and I had no reason to believe that the porcupine lodged inside it would be in any better condition.

*   *   *   *   *

NIANGON WILL, I suspect, survive the logging holocaust, and not because its generally poor form when growing in swampland may be a deterrent to some loggers. Extensive forestry programmes in planting and natural regeneration have been in force in Ghana and the Ivory Coast for many years, all geared towards the raising of trees that are the ultimate in perfection of shape and size. Modest success has already been achieved through these programmes. Perhaps a similar programme will be attempted in niangon's other home in that corner of West Africa, Liberia, should ever the appalling political situation there become stabilized.

These programmes are to be lauded, if only because they show that some attempt is being made to preserve parts of those fabled rainforests. But I, for one, hope that the boffins do not carry this cloning business too far. While the plantations of man may, through their dreary symmetry, produce perfection in trees and in timber, I think Mother Nature organizes better. She cares about the beauty of things.

Chapter 5

Iron Woods

Botanical Name — *Lophira alata*

Trade Name — Ekki

Other Names — Azobé (Ivory Coast)
Kaku (Ghana)
Bongossi (Cameroon)

Distribution — Sierra Leone to Angola

Timber — Dark purple-brown heartwood. Grain interlocked, coarse. Very difficult to work with hand tools; easier with machines. Difficult to dry – tendency to bad shakes. Must be pre-bored for nailing.

Commercial Uses — Wharves, jetties and bridges; sea defences; heavy duty flooring.

FEW, IF ANY, of the harder and heavier timbers of tropical Africa have made such an impact on the markets of Europe as ekki. From its very first appearance – when it was tried out in Liverpool in 1906 as 'red oak', of all things – its popularity has steadily increased. Today, its logs and its lumber are being exported on a regular basis from every country along the Coast.

There seems, on the surface, no real reason why this should be so. It is a well-documented fact that sawmillers the world over are sensitive souls, and the unfavourable properties of ekki are such that, in normal circumstances, they would shy like startled mares at the very thought of them. It is one of the hardest and heaviest of all African timbers. When dried, it weighs 960 to 1120 kilograms per cubic metre, while the West African mahoganies average out at 600 kilograms to the cubic metre. It is most difficult to dry successfully under any conditions as it rapidly develops severe shakes, surface checking and end splitting; its coarse interlocked grain makes it difficult to work with any but the most sophisticated of machine tools; and it cannot be nailed without pre-drilling.

Nevertheless, it has not only stood the test of time but it has prospered mightily. Ekki's saving grace has been the stability of the timber after it has been properly seasoned and its supreme durability. These two qualities combined with the fact that the wood has that sombre tone about it that seems to find such favour with civic planning authorities in colder climes, have made it a regular choice for items of outdoor construction such as park benches and rails. I once saw an ersatz totem pole made almost entirely from ekki, standing tall and proud in the teeth of a blizzard in a Canadian park.

During the latter part of the 20th century it has achieved considerable popularity worldwide, not only for heavy-duty requirements such as railway sleepers and factory flooring, but also in mixture with other West African hardwoods in parquetry for shops and offices. In the 1970's the Japanese – traditional lovers of dark-hued timbers – were showing considerable interest in its potential, while large shipments of logs were being sent from the Coast to such far-flung ports as Long Beach, California.

Ekki has also a quite astonishing resistance to all forms of natural destructive agencies when used in water, including attack by the dreaded shipworm, or teredo. For this reason, it has been used extensively in marine installations, including wharfing and all forms of sea defence construction. In West Africa, the most stable and rugged of dugout canoes are made from ekki, as are many of the sea-going long boats of the famed Fante fishermen.

It is tough and enduring timber, and when you set eyes on the source of it for the first time, you will not be a bit surprised, for you will see before you a tree that looks both tough and enduring. Ekki is one of the giants of the forest. When mature, it will often attain a height of 50 metres and a bole diameter of 1.50 metres. Only rarely will it be seen with true buttresses, and then it will generally be growing in places unsuited to it. More often, it is to be found with heavy root swellings that spread out all over the place from the base of the tree in the form of surface roots.

Experts are rarely in accord in their descriptions of the normal shape of the bole. In some publications it is stated as perfectly straight, while in others it is said to be rarely so. In my experience, shape varies according to site: I have seen great stands of ekki trees in which the majority of boles were near to being perfectly straight, while in other large concentrations I was hard pressed to find a single straight tree. I believe that soil conditions and inci-dence of light or shade must have a strong effect on the growing tree. Ekki is a sun lover; complete overhead shade will either kill it off completely or make for a very crooked tree, while dense shade with only fitful light filtering through the overhead canopy will often, in the tree's adolescent years, produce growth so rapid as it strives to reach the light that spiralling of grain is the inevitable outcome.

The bark is deeply grooved longitudinally, with long narrow scales. The colour variations can be quite startling – from a deep rusty red in the dense shade of the true rainforest to a strange sort of orange where the tree is exposed to direct sunlight on hill slopes. Between the dead outer bark and the pink inner bark there is a paper-thin layer of sulphurous yellow, a yellow that is displayed most vividly around the base of the tree and on the root swellings where the red outer layer is scraped off by animals.

The leaves are a dark and glossy green, lance-shaped, and clustered in large tufts at the ends of the branchlets. After the rain season, these fall off and new clusters of bright scarlet leaves arrive in December, making a spectacular splash of colour.

Regeneration is prolific under each tree. This is mainly due to the fact that the seed is quite a large and heavy nut with a pair of rather inadequate wings which – except in strong winds – only propel the nut to the ground directly below.

It is a very gregarious tree, and it seems quite careless as to the conditions in which it sets up home. I have seen large stands around the comparatively dry foothills of the Nimba mountains in northern Liberia, and just as many concentrated in the wet forests of the Niger delta regions. It will even put up with periodic flooding with no apparent ill effect. It can be found all over West Africa wherever there is an abundance of rainfall, and it even has a warty, twisted, scrubby little junior brother (*Lophira lanceolata*) representing it in the hot aridity of the savannah country.

It is not a tree whose timbers are used extensively by the indigenous African, although it is considered an excellent fuel because of the high wax content of its wood cells. The tribes of the delta forests make more use of it than those of the interior, for – as noted elsewhere in this chapter – it makes good canoes. Even then it has to be worked immediately after felling, otherwise it simply becomes too hard for adzing. In those wetlands fish spears and mortar pestles are often made from ekki, and in the Benin and Sapele areas of Nigeria it used to be made into ornamental wall plaques for the homes of chiefs and kings.

Many creatures eat the seeds of the ekki, which are rich in oil. Tests carried out in London at the turn of the century indicated that ekki oil would be suitable for the manufacture of soap. The forest people believe that the oil and the leaves cure leprosy, a common ailment in parts of West Africa. The afflicted person rubs the oil all over his or her body prior to retiring for the night on a bed fashioned from ekki saplings and covered with a mattress of ekki leaves.

An infusion of the root bark is believed by some tribes to be a cure for yellow fever. This, I think, may be because the yellow pigment of the inner bark – more immediately noticeable on the roots than elsewhere on the tree – is presumed to be the obvious antidote.

A close associate of ekki in many parts of its range is the appropriately named 'chicken poo-poo tree' (*Araliopsis species*). This common tree of the drier forest plateaux will often be found either in mixture with ekki or in groups of its own in close proximity to stands of ekki. Although it can occasionally reach a height of 40 metres and attain a diameter of 1.20 metres, the timber of the poo-poo tree is not of the slightest significance to either the commercial logger or the indigène. It is of muted straw colour, with a very woolly texture and an appalling smell when fresh sawn. It is hard and heavy, and it does not season at all easily. Its bark, however, is much prized by some tribes, when pulped in a mortar, as a cure for a variety of skin infections.

Another extremely hard wood I have found in association with ekki is samanta (*Bussea occidentalis*). While I have only ever come across this species in Liberia and the Ivory Coast, there are authorities who list it as being present in Ghana.

This is another of those trees whose timber is just too hard and too difficult to work, although some tribes convert saplings into tool shafts because of its strength. The tree seldom reaches more than 20 metres in height and 70 centimetres in diameter, but it is a pretty tree during the rains, when its small crown is often covered with bright yellow fragrant flowers. The seeds – flat, ovoid things about 3 centimetres long and of that old-world buff-yellow colour one used to associate with meerschaum pipes – are extremely good to eat, raw or roasted, and I have also enjoyed them in stews.

Commonly to be found in areas where there is a predominance of ekki are the various species of parinari trees. Authors of tree books on Africa cite these species as growing in virtually all soil and climatic conditions wherever there happens to be a strip of woodland between Senegal and the east coast of Africa, but most of my own memories of them are centred around the drier soil conditions of plateaux and among the foothills of mountain ranges. *Parinari excelsa* was the species most often encountered by me, and it is a very gregarious species indeed.

It is a tall tree, often reaching to 45 metres in height, but although it can attain a bole diameter of 1.50 metres, its height can make it look more slender than it actually is. But it *looks* tough, particularly when seen at the edge of a glade in the heat of the day. The grey bark gleams like gunmetal in the sunshine, giving it a stark and somewhat forbidding look – an appearance of total immobility and resistance against whatever vicissitudes fate may care to hurl against it.

Nor are its uncompromising looks a bluff. While storms may wreak their havoc around it, it is often the one left standing after their furies have abated. The peasant farmer usually has more sense than to wreck his axe and jar his elbow and shoulder bones in trying to fell it. Yet after he has felled all the other less dour species around it and set fire to them, he will still be left with the parinari – smoke-wreathed, blackened and smouldering a little around the base, but still standing erect and defiantly alive – at the end of all his efforts. Slash and burn farming is hard work in parinari country.

Its timber, too, is just about the most terrible stuff I have ever witnessed going through any sawmill. It is as heavy as lead and full of silica, so even when logs are sawn fresh from the forest, this is among the most difficult of woods to process. After logs have been left out in the sun for any length of time and become case-hardened, no sawmiller in his right mind would want anything to do with them. Yet it is an interesting species, a good looking tree in its own austere way, and its fruit is enjoyed by animal and human alike.

The fruit somewhat resembles a small rough-skinned mango in size and shape, and in some years fruit production may be prolific. The forest floor under the tree is often a carpet of fallen fruit. There is a hard nut at the centre of the drupe, but the edible bit is the surrounding fleshy part. The forest Africans eat it with avidity, but I have to confess that this is one of the very few rainforest fruits for which I have little taste, as I have found it to be too dry and floury and quite without flavour. Elephants, on the other hand, love the fruit, and so do the chimpanzees.

I was in a Land-Rover late one afternoon, travelling on the long dirt road that cuts through the heart of the Grebo forests, heading for Cape Palmas. Conditions were awful: it was the height of the rainy season, a storm was raging over me, and it was raining so hard that the windscreen wipers were just not able to cope. Inevitably, my journey came to an abrupt halt. The wooden bridge that once spanned the river in front of me in better times had been swept away, and it had taken a large chunk of the road with it. My attempt to return the way I had come was foiled almost at once when a great flare of lightning sent a colossal tree crashing across the road, effectively blocking my retreat. There was nothing for it now but to sit the night out in my vehicle.

Just before dusk the storm ceased with dramatic suddenness and the sun broke through the clouds. Delighted screams from the surrounding forest indicated the presence of chimpanzees, and I got out of the vehicle. Parinari tops towering over the roadside forest a little way off the road attracted my attention and I walked through the dripping bush towards them. I had just reached them when from the opposite end of the grove and about fifty metres from me, a small band of chimpanzees emerged. They were nine in number, six adults and three youngsters, and they were the wettest looking chimps I had ever seen in my life. They stared in my direction for a brief moment, but if they spotted me standing stock-still by the large parinari directly opposite them, they dismissed me as being of no threat to them. The ground was littered with fruit and they fell upon it eagerly, the greyish pap squirting from the sides of their mouths as they gorged themselves at speed.

I leaned against the tree, watching them. They paid no attention to me. Finally, as the loden hue of the treetops turned to black silhouette with the sinking of the sun, they scurried off silently to their secret roosting place in the depths of the wet woods. I picked up a dozen or so of the unappetizing fruit to sustain me through the long night and headed back to my own roosting place out on the road.

It was while checking out the incidence of ekki on the high slopes of the Putu Range that I first came across the steel-hard crudia tree

(*Crudia gabonensis*). So hard is the wood of this species reputed to be that I have never known anyone, black or white, to figure out any use for it. It is a tree of medium height and medium build – in fact, everything about it had a grey and medium sort of anonymity in the shade of the mighty ekkis. It would almost certainly have retained its anonymity forever as far as I was concerned had it not been for the fact that through this species I once observed the most fascinating and curious partnership in the kingdom of animals.

An ancient, dying crudia hung over the edge of the plateau. Most of its branches had long gone and it was obvious that the heart of it had gone also, cankered and rotted away through the wear and tear of time. But a ring of living wood still held the trunk upright and a few leafy branches still clung forlornly to life.

In the crotch of one of those branches was the source of the disturbance that had caused me to halt. It was a creature I had read about and heard of from hunters but had not, until that moment, ever seen. This one was about the size and coloration of the European badger, and indeed he looked very much like a badger except that he had much more white along his back. He was a very busy chap indeed, gurring and growling as he tore and ripped at the tree with fang and claw, trying to widen the hole which he had found in it. It was obvious what he was after, for the air around him dark with angry bees.

I sat down behind a large ekki, hidden from view. It was not that I was afraid I would scare him off; on the contrary, I knew the ratel, or honey badger, to have a most fearsome reputation, capable of tackling creatures as big and as terrifying as the forest buffalo when annoyed, and I had no wish to have my leg chewed off. A steady cataract of wood and bark fell to the ground as he worked, not once stopping for breath in his haste to get at the honey inside. Gradually, I became aware that there was another, equally interested, observer of the ratel's activities.

It was a bird about the size of a European blackbird, of dark greyish-green plumage on the back, white underneath, and with yellow flashes on the shoulders. This was the honeyguide, colourfully dubbed 'Indicator indicator' by the scientific establishment, both common name and scientific name relating to this little bird's habit of leading honey-loving creatures – including man, but more often the ratel – to sources of honey. The honeguide flew back and forth, yattering anxiously, its gaze darting constantly towards its hairy partner up in the tree. It was waiting for its share of the loot, and not too patiently at that. Several times it flew over to where I was hidden to confide in me, and once it even perched on the toe of my boot, quite unafraid, cocking its head to the side and fixing a large bright eye upon mine, as though asking why I did not climb the tree to lend a hand.

The grunts and growls from the crudia tree increased in intensity. A final, large chunk of wood fell to the ground and the ratel's right arm plunged in up to the armpit, to emerge a second later oozing with honey. The bird left me instantly. A piece of black honeycomb tumbled down and the bird attacked it vigorously, stabbing at the wax with its short and powerful beak. Up above it, in the fork of the tree, the honey badger was having the time of his life, scooping out huge sections of honey. Clouds of bees swarmed futilely around him. I do not know if they were of the stinging variety, as some African species are, and I did not venture close enough to find out. Even if they had been, their stings would have been ineffective against the ratel. His coat was so thick that even cobra fangs could not penetrate it. (Indeed, cobras and mambas are often included in the ratel's extensive menu when he happens upon them in his travels.)

It was getting dark by the time I left the scene. The ratel was on the ground by this time, snuffling around the tree, gobbling up any morsels of honey that remained. The swarm of bees had thinned out considerably and those that remained were flying about in a rather disconsolate manner, no longer much interested in the marauder now that their home was shattered and completely gutted of all food. Of the ratel's little feathered partner, there was no sign. She had vanished into the forest, to dream, no doubt, of finding another bonanza of honeycomb on the morrow and an equally willing and able navvy to do the dirty work for her.

*   *   *   *   *

I HAVE KNOWN ekki all over West Africa, from the dark wet forests of Cameroon and southern Nigeria, where the constant humidity and drenching rain transforms the redness of its coat to a rather sombre mocha hue, to the high slopes of Liberia and the Ivory Coast, where the rust-red glow of its bark seems to spring from the iron-rich soil in which it grows.

It is a tree that is much in love with life. It likes the company of its fellows, and its tops resound daily to the sound of the birds and the chatter of monkeys throughout the dry months. You feel safe, comfortable somehow, when spending the night on the forest floor under the ekki tree, with its mighty arms spreading over you and its great frame, as enduring as time itself, anchored to the ferrous rocks beside and under you. You sleep snug and secure here, knowing that in long aeons past, some primitive ancestor of yours most probably slept here too, equally snug, equally secure, under the protective cloak of this, Africa's king of the ironwoods.

Chapter 6

The Ordeal Tree

Botanical Names   –   *Erythrophleum ivorense/E.
                       suaveolens*

Trade Name   –   Tali

Other Names   –   Sasswood (Liberia)
                      Erun (Nigeria)
                      Kassa (Zaire)

Distribution   –   Sierra Leone to Zambia

Timber   –   Reddish-brown to dark brown.
                      Coarse texture, interlocked grain.
                      Lustrous. Hard and very heavy. Very
                      strong. Great resistance to decay and
                      boring insects. Difficult to work, but
                      turns well.

Commercial Uses   –   Parquet flooring in mixture with
                      other species. Most types of exterior
                      carpentry.

IN MOST REFERENCE books the two species *Erythrophleum ivorense* and *E. suaveolens* are listed together, so little is there to distinguish their timbers. Even to the eyes of the professional tropical dendrologist, there has always been an element of confusion, so nearly identical in appearance are the standing trees. The most obvious variations are that *E. suaveolens* does not grow to such heights and dimensions as *E. ivorense*, and it sticks to the drier areas along the northern fringes of the high-forest belt, while *E. ivorense* is a species of the wetter southern forests. However, there is no clearly delineating line either, for the ranges of the two species tend to overlap quite a bit, with the two often found growing together. For simplicity's sake, therefore, I shall take a leaf out of the logger's book and refer to the two species together as 'tali' or 'sasswood'.

Tali is a large tree. The longer bole lengths and the greater diameters are to be found in the more southerly evergreen forests. This is not, I feel, purely a species characteristic: all trees of whatever species growing at the extremities of their normal range tend to have neither the height, the volume, nor the symmetry of bole attained by them in their true habitat.

Nevertheless, even at the furthest reaches of its range tali can attain a height of 30 metres and a diameter of 1.20 metres. It has short, thick, rounded buttresses. The bark on mature trees is very rough and of a dull greyish-umbrine hue. The bole is rarely straight beyond the first 10 metres of its length. Old trees – particularly those growing in open clearings or in light secondary forest – are often rotten at the base, with well-developed burrs protruding from the bottom part of the trunk. The crown is very dense and dark green, somewhat mushroom-shaped but with large spreading branches. The flowers, though densely packed throughout the crown during the December harmattan, are quite difficult to see, either from the ground or from the air, for they are tiny and of such an indistinct yellowish-brown as to allow them to melt into obscurity amidst the sombre density of the leaves. However, even if one cannot actually see them, one is aware that they must be out for their strong smell of honey has the crowns throbbing with the hum of bees at this time of the year.

The fruits are flat, leathery pods about eight centimetres long by three wide, containing half-a-dozen seeds. Even after the pods open they remain clearly visible on the branchlets at the top of the tree for quite a long time, with the seeds still attached to the inner casings and only falling gradually to the ground in dribs and drabs.

The dark brown timber is streaked black here and there and looks rather dour when fresh sawn. With exposure, it very gradually mellows into a warmer chocolate lustre. It is one of the strongest timbers in Africa, being highly resistant to decay and the predations of boring termites. Before the era of the chainsaw arrived to signal the beginning of the end for the rainforests, tali was quite common, especially in the wetter parts, and it was much used locally for most types of heavy construction, from bridges over rivers, to railway sleepers and harbour installations. For smaller items of domestic use it was found to be much too difficult to work. In addition, the very fine sawdust it produced inside mills was a severe irritant. However, with the advent of more sophisticated techniques and equipment more use is being made of the timber now. It turns well, can produce a surprisingly attractive finish, and is ideal for flooring for it has a high resistance to wear. Now used a lot throughout Europe, in mixture with lighter coloured but equally hard-wearing African species such as the sulphur-yellow opepe (*Nauclea diderrichii*) and the creamy-white odoko (*Scottellia coriacea*), it makes for the most attractive of parquet flooring.

Tali has always been common throughout tropical Africa, from Sierra Leone to far-off Uganda. It could be quite scattered and solitary in some places but prolific in others. Liberia was full of it, and there were parts of Nigeria and Cameroon in which it was, at one time, very common.

The tali is a strange tree which I find hard to come to terms with. My whole life has revolved around trees, both in the tropics and in the temperate zone. Mostly – indeed, with only three exceptions – I am happiest when in the company of trees. There is something that I find immensely satisfying, deeply comforting about trees, whether I am walking among them or sleeping under their sheltering embrace. I confess that I dislike mangroves for the stinking squelching mud that is their habitat and the relentless swarms of biting flies that inhabit their forbidding environment. But this is a physical dislike, an understandable dislike. Less easy to understand is the reason for my dislike of the Sitka spruce of the northern climes.

Since my early years with the Forestry Commission in Scotland, I have never failed to find myself overcome by a deepening disquiet each time I walk through a forest of this spiky stranger from the wastes of Alaska. I find something decidedly spooky about the dark, silent chambers of a Sitka spruce forest, a funereal stillness in which no sound is heard and the only moving thing to be seen is the occasional tiny coal tit slipping silently through the branches.

I would be the first to acknowledge that it is a completely illogical fear, something perhaps inherited from my Hebridean forebears; the primeval association of still black woods with malignant spirits, the creepy sensations that chill the spine and raises the hair on the back of the neck, putting urgency into the step while at the same time turning the knee joints to jelly. There is the ineradicable feeling that witches and werewolves are watching your every step and that somewhere ahead of you in the gloom black-caped assassins are lying in wait. I have walked many, many miles in my youth through Sitka spruce woods, but I would have walked many miles further to avoid spending even one single night in their sepulchral company.

Forests of tali affect me in much the same way. I remember the first tali tree I ever saw. It was in Nigeria, on the edge of a dark and forbidding swamp in the Niger Delta. I was unaware until some time later that one of its names was tali, nor did I even then associate this tree with the infamous sasswood, but I knew from the very beginning that there was something not quite right about it. I didn't have to be told: I just *knew*. There seemed to be an invisible sort of pall around it, an almost tangible aura of evil, and when I eventually discovered its connection with the legendary 'trial by ordeal', I was the least surprised man in all of Africa.

Not all plants of such deadly reputation are quite so recognizable as being such. Indeed, some of the most poisonous plants in the world are among the most beautiful to look at. The common laburnum delights the gardener's eye with its long sprays of golden blossoms in the spring, the belladonna lily is a greenhouse favourite with its fragrant flowers of virginal pink, and everyone knows and loves the woodland foxglove. Yet all of those plants are extremely poisonous in one form or another. Even that old familiar the mistletoe, so beloved at Christmas, contains a highly lethal level of lectins and peptidic toxins that would have done the Good King Wenceslas no good at all had a vengeful page dropped a dozen or so of the little pearly berries into the monarch's plum pudding mix.

To most of the timber trade the *Erythrophleum* species are known as 'tali' or (occasionally) 'missanda'. To most indigenous forest Africans it is the 'sasswood' or 'the ordeal tree'. By the early part of the 20th century the sasswood reputation had spread far beyond the shores of Africa and every boy who had ever read an adventure story with a Dark Continent background would have been familiar with its infamous properties. The basic principles of the 'ordeal' were also well enough known. Put in its simplest terms, the accused was made to drink a decoction from the tree bark. If he survived, he was innocent, but if he died, he was guilty. There was, of course, a great deal more to it than that, and although I write mainly from hearsay, I did once witness someone die from sasswood poisoning. It was a moving experience, not only for the victim but for we who were forced to watch her die.

There were two methods generally employed for the extraction of the poison from the bark, and each was simplicity itself. The method used depended entirely upon which one happened to be the traditional custom for a particular tribal area. In the first, a few pieces of bark would be boiled for twenty minutes or so in water and the mixture allowed to cool before administering. In the second method, small pieces of bark would be pounded to a pulp in a mortar made from the sacred 'akee apple' (*Blighia sapida*). The resulting mush would then be scraped out and infused overnight in cold water, as one would prepare barley for soup. The solution was known as 'red water', and its death-dealing properties were rightly feared. The intensity of the redness – and therefore the degree of potency of the poison – seemed to depend greatly upon the age of the tree from which the bark was obtained: young trees, with their thicker, more pulpy bark, produced a mellow-looking amber-rosé liquid, while infusion or boiling of the thinner, drier bark of old mature trees resulted in a fluid the colour of a good vintage claret. That which was obtained from younger trees was reputed to be much less toxic than the potion from old trees and, in most cases, was the one preferred in 'ordeal trials', for it gave the accused more time to protest his innocence. It prolonged the trial, and therefore the talking, the accusations, the denials, the litigation marathons so enjoyed by 'bush lawyers'. The darker water from the old trees had a well-merited reputation for killing the accused stone dead within a very short time of swallowing the mixture, thus spoiling all the fun for everyone concerned, including, no doubt, the victim himself.

Attempts – never completely convincing – have been made from time to time to analyse the poisonous principles of the bark. I am neither a man of medicine nor an analytical chemist, and it would therefore be presumptuous of me to attempt to go into detail on a subject which is, as yet, only imperfectly understood even by scientists. Suffice to say that, although in most ordeal trials involving sasswood it was only the bark that was used, every single part of the tree, from the leaves and flowers to the roots, was considered to be of the most extreme toxicity by the forest Africans. While the drastic effects upon the victim were apparently due mainly to the presence of an alkaloid erythrophleine, plenty of other nasties have also been isolated within the bark by scientists. Poisoning by sasswood would appear to be similar in effect to poisoning by digitalis, the victim experiencing great difficulty in breathing and being racked by severe convulsions before death by cardiac arrest ends it all.

There is no doubt whatever that 'trial by ordeal' involving sasswood has resulted in many deaths in Africa. It was a trial held when all else failed, to prove an accused innocent or guilty. The 'crime' might have been a really serious one, such as the stealing of a neighbour's goat, or a very minor one, such as the stealing of a neighbour's wife. Only when the matter had degenerated into an insoluble dispute would the witchdoctor be called in and a trial by ordeal arranged.

Oddly enough, few had to be tied down to have the stuff force-fed into their gullets through funnels. Often, the accused would actually demand that he be allowed to undergo the sasswood ordeal, even if, secretly, he was fully aware of his own guilt. This was not only foolish bravado on his part: the bush African was a fatalist. Tomorrow was another day . . . what was to be would be . . . and besides, with any luck he would be able to bribe the witchdoctor to adulterate the mixture. There was also the fact that the ordeal was undoubtedly grand theatre, and for once in his humdrum life he was to be the star attraction, even if it killed him.

For the trial would rarely be held behind closed doors. Justice had to be seen to be done, and from the chief's and witchdoctor's point of view, it made good political sense to ensure that all of their subject should see it being done. From the beginning of time, there have been few things more guaranteed to whet the appetite of the human race than the knowledge that something grisly is about to happen to one of their fellows and that they are going to be privileged to witness it. The Africans of the bush are no different. This was a spectacle that gripped the imagination then as do some ghastly soap operas in our present television society. When the drums beat out the news that a trial by ordeal was in the offing, the people of the forest were going to make damned sure they were not going to miss it. They came from far and near to see it, bringing their children and their aged grannies along with them.

It was as great a social occasion as the Epsom Derby. Ladies put on their finest and the men combed the swamps to obtain the best quality palm wine for the Big Day. The accused was sat on a special high stool or stand in the middle of the village compound where everyone could see him. He would be given some rice and a piece of kolanut to eat. 'Lawyers' for the defence and prosecution would then be agreed upon by accused and accuser, and during the proceedings impassioned pleas by the defendant's relatives and friends on his behalf would be heard. At each interval the accused would be given a cup of 'red water' to drink. Should he at any time vomit up the rice and the kolanut he would immediately be pronounced innocent, while failure to do so would almost certainly mean that his fate was sealed.

'The trick', explained my friend Dr Malcolm McDonald, a man with much knowledge of the mystic world of the African witchdoctor, 'was to swallow the muck as quickly as possible. Those convinced of their innocence had no fear of drinking it. They would drink it quickly and the stomach would just a quickly reject it. Those knowing they were guilty would be much more reluctant to drink. They would sip the potion slowly and thus give their organs more time to absorb it.'

Even in my day, poisoning by one means or another was a popular way of getting back at those who had happened to become the object of a person's wrath. I have even known the occasional expatriate to fall victim, usually because he had been guilty of two-timing his current lover. But in such cases, it was rarely fatal, and almost never intended to be so: more often it was only a warning that the errant lover had better behave himself in future. Sasswood was never used in such exercises. It was too easy to detect, and there were plenty of other poisons just as toxic but which had the advantage that they could not be detected by taste.

Sasswood was, however, quite often used as an arrow poison in hunting. In mixture with a decoction from the woody vine *Stropanthus hispidus* (commonly found growing in secondary forest near sasswood trees) – the seeds of which contain very high concentrations of extremely poisonous cardiac glycosides – an arrowhead thus doctored would flatten an elephant in record time. The sasswood paste would be smeared on the arrowhead first and then the viscous *stropanthus* extract applied. The latter dried like paint over the sasswood, holding it in place yet losing none of its own effectiveness. Great care had to be exercised during application of both or the would-be hunter was liable to find himself hoist with his own petard.

I once had a geriatric Tiv night-watchman who, while on duty, was always armed with a fragile-looking bow and a quiver full of innocuous-looking arrows, little more than elongated bamboo splinters. He was regarded as nothing but a senile, bumbling joke by my white colleagues, who could not understand why, at this time when there was such a spate of burglaries on expatriate houses in the area, my own house remained miraculously untargetted. Rather curious myself, I asked the old man one evening when I had a few of those same colleagues over for drinks. Without reply, he fitted an arrow into his bow and aimed it at a scrawny, rabid-looking brown cur some distance away which had, of late, taken to sneaking into my compound to mutilate my ducks and chickens. The wretched creature was already dying a split second later when it spun round to see what had stung its rump. The effects of the combination of sasswood and stropanthus was instantaneous, and no one laughed at the old man after that demonstration.

Although none have captured the imagination of the outside world quite like the sasswood, there are, of course, plenty of other tree species of poisonous repute to be found within the African rainforests. One of the lesser-known species is the 'death-devil tree', and it is so greatly feared by some tribes that none of their members will even touch it. The death-devil tree, known to the world of dendrologists by the resounding title of '*Bersama abyssinica var. paullinioides*', is a skinny, insignificant little tree of the secondary forests and the river banks. It has equally insignificant greenish-white, sweetly-scented flowers. Roots and fruit are highly poisonous, and potions from them have been used for poisoning people in Sierra Leone, Liberia and the Ivory Coast. The 'breakback tree' (*Dichapetalum toxicarium*) is another small and harmless-looking tree of the secondary forest whose innocent appearance conceals the virulence of the poison contained within. The round, mango-shaped fruits contain two seeds: the pulp surrounding them is quite edible, but the kernels are very poisonous. No one has yet completely identified the toxic properties, but the effects are said to be similar to that of poisoning by strychnine. While its main use was certainly in the killing of rats, there is no doubt that in the past it has also been used successfully on human beings who happened to become surplus to requirement for one reason or another.

Another very common and equally insignificant little tree is the aptly-named 'executioner' (*Mareya micrantha*). Found mainly as an understorey tree in closed or secondary forest, it is rarely more than 15 metres in height and it is covered with masses of small, fragrant, cream-coloured flowers in the latter part of the dry season. The small scarlet fruits are as bitter as gall, and potions from these and the leaves were not only used as active poisons but as a purgative so violent that it resulted in many deaths all over West Africa. It was probably the laxative to end all laxatives, and dreaded everywhere by prospective patients.

All these are straightforward poisons that might be used by anyone wishing to get rid of an enemy or an unwanted person. They could even be used by women. There were certain tribes (particularly in Liberia) in which girls, upon reaching puberty, would be taken to a secret place in the depths of the forest by selected senior women for a two-year course on what might – for want of a better phrase – be called 'The Meaning of Life'. During this time they would be taught everything that the old women could teach them. They learned all the skills of cooking, the art of lovemaking in all its forms, the appropriate plants to use for various types of sickness, and they were given comprehensive instruction on how to prepare virulent poisons from certain plants against the event that their future husbands might ever be tempted to step out of line.

All these poisons were for the use of women as well as for the men. But the sasswood was a man's poison. None but the men dared to use it, and even then ordinary mortals might only use it as an arrow poison. None but the witchdoctors were allowed to administer it in trial by ordeal.

Poisons are, of course, obtainable from plants other than trees. Many come from vines. Most of those, too, had routine uses: on arrow-tips for hunting; for the killing of mice, rats, headlice; as purgatives and abortifacients. But there was one climbing vine that, during the middle years of the 20th century, achieved almost the same level of international notoriety as the sasswood. This was the 'Calabar bean' plant (*Physostigma venenosum*).

The Calabar bean plant has a sinister reputation. It is nothing more than a woody vine with large floppy leaves, something like a cross between the honeysuckle and the European columbine. Although it has been named the 'Calabar' bean, it is in fact to be found in almost every part of the hotter and wetter regions of the West

African rainforest, despite colonial foresters originally encountering it in the Calabar area of southern Nigeria.

The seeds are deadly poisonous, chocolate-brown, about three centimetres long, and look something like large coffee beans. They contain many toxic alkaloids and have often been used in trials by ordeal like the sasswood. The victim would be made to drink water containing the crushed beans and – as with the sasswood – if he survived, he was considered innocent, while his death was a presumption of guilt. The poison acted almost instantly on the spinal cord, causing paralysis of the limbs and heart muscles. Hundreds of deaths from Calabar bean ingestion were reported during one spate of poisoning in Zaire even as short a time ago as 1959, and there is little doubt in my mind that the bean has been responsible for probably more deaths than even the sasswood.

There was a time when the Calabar bean was cultivated and sold in markets, though under colonial rule this was strictly forbidden. I have never seen them for sale in any of the former French or British possessions, although I was often assured that they could be purchased 'under the counter' in some places. I was, of course, aware that a bean extract was used by the forest people for all the usual things: the killing of rodents and lice, for the treatment of a variety of ailments including rheumatism, by hunters as an arrow poison. Modern medicine has even secured a drug from it called physostigmine, which is used in post-operative treatment to excite peristalsis, and is also used in the treatment of tetanus, glaucoma, and so on. I have found the plant growing wild – most often, strangely enough, in areas where the sasswood was most prevalent – and I have also seen it as a cultivated plant around villages in the interior. But I have only once come upon it openly for sale in a market, and that was in the Grand Cess area of central Liberia, a country that has never been burdened by the irksome restrictions of colonial rule. 'For back pain,' explained the market woman enigmatically when I asked her for what purpose they would be used. Maybe so. It was perhaps sheer coincidence that not long afterwards a sensational and very public trial was held in the neighbouring county, after which, following allegations of witchcraft, cannibalism, ordeal trials and ritual poisoning, a prominent public figure was hanged along with a few of his associates. Sasswood and the Calabar bean featured prominently in the accusations of the prosecuting counsel.

*   *   *   *   *

WHEN I WAS in a position to carry out sawmill tests on a variety of previously little-known African tree species, I was constantly on the lookout on my travels for anything unusual with which to test both the saw-teeth and the patience of my long-suffering sawmill manager.

On the edge of a timber landing one day I spotted a tali log which had evidently been discarded as defective, for it had a large hole at one end. Two big gnarled burrs jutted out from the surface of the log. I studied them for a minute or two, then called over a chain-saw operator working on some logs at the far end of the landing. Within minutes, he had the burrs neatly removed. Somewhat to my surprise, they were quite sound. Even more to my surprise, they were two of the most beautiful pieces of timber I had ever seen. Of perfect coffee-table size, each cut surface was a convoluted twining of the most exquisite figuring of hues – orange and brown and green and gold and purple and red – a phantasmagoria of colour and design such as might have been dreamt up by the great Chinese pottery artists of old. The pieces polished beautifully, and they were soon installed as much-admired tables in my living room. I began to tour abandoned landings within the forest, looking for similar reject logs, and, as we were right in the heart of tali forest here, they were not hard to find. Soon, orders were coming in from all over the place for those highly decorative tables.

It was a year or so later that I dropped in at the home of a newly-married friend in eastern Liberia. It was midday, very hot, and I was enjoying a cold beer. A Waterford crystal vase full of flowers stood on a little table near me. My hostess was a newcomer to Africa. She had been a keen gardener back home in Europe and she was plainly entranced by the profusion and the beauty of the wild flowers growing in the encroaching forest around the perimeter of the compound. Early each morning, just as the sun was beginning its climb

70

over the treetops, she would set off with her basket and her garden shears to collect her day's supply of flowers for the house.

Today's selection was certainly a pretty one, vetches of a satiny purple clustered thick and droopy-headed on their stalks, very reminiscent of the cultivated sweet peas of Europe.

She saw me looking at them. 'Lovely, aren't they?' she remarked. 'Do you know what they are?'

I smiled somewhat wryly at her. 'Those', I replied, 'are known locally as 'Flowers of the Woodland Spirits'. The plant itself was better known as the Calabar bean. And the table on which your vase is standing is one which I gave your husband some time ago. It is made from the wood of the sasswood tree.'

'What intriguing names they have out here!' she exclaimed. She fingered one of the flowers gently, then asked: 'Are the beans good to eat?'

I looked at my glass. A fly was struggling in the amber liquid. I fished it out and crushed it in the ashtray beside me. 'Not unless you're tired of life,' I informed her cheerily.

Chapter 7

Man Sticks

Botanical Name	–	*Cylicodiscus gabunensis*
Trade Name	–	Okan
Other Name	–	Denya (Ghana)
Distribution	–	The rainforests, from Ghana to Gabon.
Timber	–	Greenish-brown when fresh felled, becoming a very dark and sombre brown on exposure. Very hard and very heavy. Coarse of texture but lustrous. Works, stains and polishes quite well, but can only be nailed with pre-drilling. Often distorts badly on drying.
Commercial Uses	–	All forms of heavy construction work.

O NE OF THE first of the real rainforest giants I ever saw being felled was the okan. It was a colossal specimen, and four Ibo axeman were positioned around it, swinging away lustily with their axes. The clang of the razor-sharp blades hitting the wood was like steel ringing on steel, and it was a sound that seemed to reverberate up and down, up and down throughout the length of the trunk, so hard was the wood. Only the finest of axe-heads could have withstood that degree of shock, and these were imported and made of the finest quality steel. Even so, this stuff was obviously much harder than anything I had ever encountered before. As I watched, one of the men threw his axe to the ground in disgust. The edge of the blade was shattered. In my many years experience of axe felling, I had never seen this happen before.

Okan is a tree that one can never imagine being small, a tender young sapling like other trees, at the mercy of tiny weevils and browsing ruminants. When it suddenly appears in front of you in the forest, standing there in all its enormity, dwarfing everything around it, the thought that first springs to mind is that it must have been planted there by some pagan deity, exactly as it now stands, without having to go through the time-consuming effort of growing up from the sapling stage as others did. Its rather gloomy aspect in no way lessens this first impression that some dark divinity has had a hand in its existence, for there is a monkish severity in this initial appearance ideally suited to the pluvial density of the evergreen forests of Africa's West Coast.

Okan is listed in many works as being quite common everywhere, but I have never found this to be the case. It was certainly more common in the Nigeria of my youth than anywhere else I have been, but even there it tended to be of a solitary disposition, scattered, rather then clustered in stands anywhere. Despite its size, it was a tree that sometimes went unnoticed in the heart of the forest, perhaps because the tendency of its dark brown bark to flake off in long, scarious strips helped to soften the severity of its outline and allow it to merge with its surroundings.

The trunk is as straight as a ramrod, and it can grow to an incredible 60 metres in height and 3.5 metres in diameter. Although the crown is huge and rather sprawling, it is not as dense as one might expect of such a large tree. One distinctive feature throughout the dry season is the mass of dark-brown pods, a metre long by about 4 centimetres wide, that hang from the branches like giant baubles from a Christmas tree; pods which eventually open to release long, papery seeds that spiral off slowly and clumsily in the still forest, like termites taking to the air for the first time.

It is a species that is quite devoid of buttresses, even the largest specimens being equipped with little more than gentle swellings at the base of the tree where the roots bulge out. Nevertheless, the okan is rarely affected by even the most violent of the rainseason's early storms. It is the most windfirm of trees. Its roots are as sturdy as the tree itself; spread far and wide, they maintain a very firm grip on the ancient latosols of Mother Africa.

The wood of the okan is ranked among the hardest and heaviest in all of Africa. There is a sharp distinction between sapwood and heartwood: the sapwood is an odd sort of greyish pink in colour and the heartwood, when the tree is fresh-felled, is a pleasing dark amber-brown with an underlying olive-green tinge to it. It is very slow to dry, and the longer it dries the harder it gets. Its strength values are very high indeed, being rated as comparable to those of the South American demerara greenheart. The grain is very much interlocked but, in spite of this, the timber works surprisingly well with all manner of machine tools. It is a timber that has been accepted around the markets of Europe with varying degrees of enthusiasm since the early 1920's, but its weight and its hardness limits its uses to heavy duty flooring and wharf decking and piling. It is extremely durable and virtually impervious to fungal and insectivorous attack or fungal degradation.

The timber is far too heavy and hard to be of much interest to the forest dwellers. Spear- and paddle-heads are occasionally carved from softer sapwood limbs that fall from the crown, but the forest African's abiding interest in this species lies in certain properties it is reputed to have which make it dearer to his soul than any spears or paddles could ever possibly be.

Okan is one of a few rainforest trees known to the forest African as 'man sticks'. Here and there in the heart of the forest, particularly where the tree is encountered by the side of the path, the bark around its base will often be found scarred through repeated removal of sections of bark by passers-by. Their reasons for doing so reflect the African's obsession with 'power': 'power' in the physical, 'strong-man' sense, and – even more important – 'power' in matters sexual. An infusion from the bark of an old okan will hasten recovery from a debilitating illness, and it will give a man the power to complete an arduous and unpleasant task, while an infusion from the bark of a young tree – taken shortly before the time the effect is required – is universally regarded as certain to produce the most formidable of erections on the least likely of subjects.

A number of other rainforest species, large and small, are revered for their aphrodisiac properties. One of these, *Newtonia aubrevillei*, is an understorey tree of poor shape and narrow, high-reaching buttresses. The bark is grey, thin and fibrous; a slash slowly exudes a clear and very sticky gum which smells strongly of sperm. Undoubtedly because of this characteristic, the species is held in high esteem by the forest people, who regard it as blessed with powerful aphrodisiac properties. Some tribes call it the 'man-power tree'. Most Newtonia boles tend to look as though they have been chewed by animals, so scarred are they by the regular removal of bark. It is believed that chewing the bark is the key to successful intercourse.

Be that as it may, Newtonia timber is useless. The stem habit is invariably so poor that obtaining worthwhile lengths from the bole of any tree would be well nigh impossible, and in any case the timber is extremely susceptible to fungal attack. The only time I have every seen it sawn – in a large sawmill, for experimental purposes – the stench from the logs as they were processed was of such penetrating foulness that the whole place stank like a fifth-rate Levantine fornicatorium for ages afterwards.

The kola tree is another 'man stick' (*Cola nitida*). It, too, is usually an understorey species. It never grows to any size that would produce worthwhile timber, and it is usually to be found as a rather anonymous dark green shrub in the shade of the forest or, sometimes, as a cultivated shrub in farm enclaves and village compounds.

It is protected by those who live in the forest, and there are usually strict tribal laws against the cutting down and the damaging of kola trees. This is because of its fruit, the kolanut, which is a much valued commodity all over West Africa. On any market stall wherever one goes along the Coast kolanuts can be found, little heaps of them on tables, or in containers of all sizes, from mugs to buckets to huge pans full of them, for sale or for barter, either singly or in quantity. Kolanut is as much part of the currency of the Coast as the dollar and the naira and the franc. I have even seen a young prostitute's services purchased with kolanut: ten kolanut she charged for the night.

The kolanut is about the size and shape of a brazil nut. It is most astringent and bitter as gall. While no research – to my knowledge at least – has yet been carried out to verify the ancient beliefs about the properties of okan and Newtonia bark, one is on much firmer ground with the kolanut. Scientific tests have found it contains far greater quantities of caffeine and theobromine than tea or coffee, and its importance as a stimulant has now been recognized in the world of medicine. In the rainforests of the Africa of my day a visitor to a village would invariably be offered kolanut and a tumblerful of illicit gin by the chief on arrival to show that he had been accepted as a guest of the village, and it would have been considered a grave discourtesy to decline this offering.

Neither the gin nor the kolanut were to my taste: the 'gin', which was raw alcohol distilled from sugar cane, smelt awful and tasted worse, while the first bite through a kolanut seemed instantly to evaporate every drop of moisture from the mouth, leaving it as dry as the inside of an Egyptian tomb. However, one simply drank and chewed to avoid causing offence.

On the odd occasion there would be other offerings to the particularly favoured guest, offerings which were even less easy to decline. Apart from its known properties of helping a man get through a long hard day in forest and farm, kolanut had the reputation of being able to help him through a sleepless night. Thus, in some of the more remote tribal areas a guest to the village might find himself heading for his room with a container of illicit gin, a pocketful of kolanuts, and a maiden or two to help ward off the mosquitoes during the long dreary hours of the African night on his stick-bed.

It was hell in the tropics in those days.

Yet, while kola gave 'man power', and this included power in the sexual sense, the emphasis was always on staying power. The eating of kolanut gave extra physical and mental energy. It was never regarded as an aphrodisiac in the true sense of the word. It was purely an energy-booster, used as a sexual aid only when all else failed or none of the other recognized philtres were available.

Ozouga (*Sacoglottis gabonensis*), on the other hand, was used purely for its aphrodisiac properties. This most wierdly shaped of all the trees in the rainforest has just got to be the least likely-looking source of erotogenic material in the whole of the tree world. It looks as if it might have been created as an obscure celestial joke somewhere around the Andromeda galaxy following the Big Bang at the birth of time. Nevertheless, it is regarded by the forest African as containing the most powerful of all aphrodisiacs.

Ozouga can be a very large tree indeed, growing to a height of 40 metres and, occasionally, more. But even at such a height it looks squat and ugly, for its bole is truly enormous. It has been measured at 4.5 metres above the buttresses, and I am sure that I have seen specimens of far greater diameter, although I did not measure them. However, although Unwin reports sample logs to have been offered for sale on the Liverpool market in 1906 at three pence or six pence per superficial foot as 'a mahogany of mild texture and fairly good colour', it has never been a species to excite the attention of the timber trade. The reason for this indifference would become obvious to anyone who has ever seen the ozouga growing in its native habitat, for it is an extraordinary looking tree.

The buttresses are of every shape and contortion known to botany. No two trees are alike in this respect. It is true that, on the odd occasion, buttresses may consist of little more than wide-spreading lumpy roots, but mostly they are great slabs of wood, transversely ridged, thin and high-reaching, often extending far up the tree and merging with the bole in thick ligneous varicosity. Around the base of the tree the buttresses are the most twisted, convoluted plates of wood imaginable, anything up to three metres tall, and in old specimens they spread in all directions, an incredible maze of high wooden walls that provide splendid shelter and sleeping quarters for some of the rainforest's less pleasant denizens.

The trunk can be virtually any shape that one can possibly envisage in a tree. I have seen trunks that are as tall and straight and cylindrical as that of any mahogany, but this is extremely rare. Much more often they are squat, gnarled, crooked, knotty, angular, or just a general mixture of every undesirable characteristic ever found in trees. The bark is a dark reddish-brown (lighter on immature trees), the living bark quite thin but covered in long shaggy scales that give the bole a most untidy appearance, like the body of a Tibetan yak. When slashed with a machete, a most eerie hissing sound can be heard from within the tree and the wound exudes a clear, sticky, pinkish-brown sap that has a cloying sugary odour to it, like the smell of a deserted beehive.

The trunk generally branches early into a huge wide-spreading and circular-shaped fairly open crown and regeneration under it is therefore quite prolific. This does not, however, apply to the regeneration of other species: the ozouga is the most gregarious of all African rainforest trees, but it does not tolerate other species growing around it.

The leaves are a dull green in colour, with a hint of grey wherever the sun happens to hit them. They are leathery and similar in length and shape to the European bay laurel. The flowers are tiny and profuse, covering the crown in a beige blanket all through the dry season from mid-November to early April. The fruit is also to be found in copious quantity throughout the rain season. It is of roughly the same size and shape as the edible European walnut, with a woody husk covered in walnut-like nodules and usually containing three seeds. Between the husk and the smooth, shiny green epidermis is a layer of fleshy pulp which is sweet and edible. During the growing season the fruit exudes droplets of clear honey-smelling liquid, resulting in the crowns of the trees to be swarming with bees and ants, while over the ground below a dancing, flowing, iridescent cloud of some of the most colourful butterflies in the world feed on the rotting fruit.

Ozouga is a tree that can be found growing just about anywhere along the shores of the Gulf of Guinea, wherever there is a sufficiently high rainfall. (Likewise, a very closely related species, *Sacoglottis amazonica*, is to be found in abundance across the Atlantic in the American rainforests.) The tree is not regarded with much favour by either the logger or the silviculturist. The former eyes it askance because of its poor shape, and the latter dislikes it because its massive crown and its extreme gregariousness means that it dominates hugh chunks of the rainforest to the detriment of the more valuable timber species. In addition, it is a tree that is well-nigh impossible to eradicate by fair means or foul. Cut it down, and shoots will spring up an hundred-fold in its place, either through regeneration or coppicing. Other traditional control methods, such as ring-barking and poisoning, are also rendered totally ineffective by the heavily fluted stem and deeply ingrown bark.

Africa has had ozouga for around 65 million years, and it is unlikely that mere man will be able to pull the plug on it, even with his chainsaws.

Nevertheless, ozouga wood has always been a favourite with the inhabitants of the forest. The timber is, in fact, quite good. It is of a most pleasing dark-red hue, tending to be rather plain in appearance, only rarely with any noticeable figuring. It is tough, hard and heavy, as well as tight of grain, but it is all the same quite easy to work with both hand and machine tools. It is also fairly resistant to decay, so there is little doubt that only its very poor shape has prevented ozouga from making a substantial impact on the export market over the decades.

However, poor shape has rarely been a drawback to the forest pitsawyer when nothing else has been available, and this is one tree that was always used extensively by the coastal tribes. They made canoes from it and they reduced it to plank form for building and general carpentry purposes. At the turn of the century, many coastal trading stations were built almost exclusively from ozouga, while in more recent times, now that logging and farming have decimated the forests around the coastal towns and cities, ozouga and mangrove have become the mainstay of the firewood industry, and ozouga has been found to be without peer in the making of charcoal.

Most important of all for the forest African was the esteem in which ozouga was held in matters sexual. This species was regarded to be the source of the most powerful aphrodisiac of all.

While the preparation of philtres from the bark of the okan tended to be of a somewhat esoteric nature, there was nothing secretive about the philtres prepared from the ozouga. A small segment of the bark would simply be added to one's palm wine, and *voilà*! 'It makes the wine taste bitter, but it makes it taste good,' one would be told. Then the connoisseur in such matters would add: 'It gives a man power to take ten women in one night or one woman ten times in one night.'

The addition of a piece of ozouga bark certainly imparted a marvellous piquancy to one's palm wine, particularly when the wine had been drawn from a 'young tree' and was therefore almost unbearably sweet to the palate. I suppose this would be much the same principle as that of adding angostura bitters to gin in more 'enlightened' societies.

While palm wine prepared in this manner is certainly most pleasant, I have never, alas, experienced the surge of raw primal lust that was supposed to engulf one following the drinking of it. It is probable that the circumstances had something to do with it. I would usually be in the wrong company – invariably black hunters stinking of rotting swamp water and the slime and gore and faecal matter adhering to their bodies from the hunt of the previous night. In such circumstances, it would have taken a lot more than a piece of tree bark in my drink to have aroused any carnal urges. Had I been offered the stuff, say, during the early 1970's when I found myself in Hollywood and introduced to gaggles of quite the most glamorous young ladies it has every been my good fortune to meet, God alone knows what the future might have held for me.

Okan, Newtonia, kola and ozouga. Four species with absolutely nothing in common except this strange link to man's insatiable obsession with being able to out-perform his peers in every aspect of life, whether on the battlefield, in the sports arena, in the board-room or the bed. 'Power' in West Africa is everything. I have known okan and kolanut to be taken in tribal conflicts by warriors going into battle and by footballers before an important match. Axemen never started a day's felling without either or both giving strength and staying-power to a man. But Newtonia and ozouga were taken for one reason only, and that was 'to give man power with woman'. In the African rainforest, this was the greatest power of all, for a man who failed to satisfy a woman in bed was not a man at all.

Newtonia bark was stripped from the tree and eaten while sappy. Only fresh was it considered effective. Ozouga bark, however, was considered effective regardless of its age. Unwin reports having seen a sheet of ozouga bark three feet long being sold for five shillings at Calabar market in Nigeria in the early 1930's, and I have seen it for sale in great rolls in city, town and village markets in every country along the Coast from Liberia to Cameroon. When its reputation as an aphrodisiac was so widely accepted, not only by the people of the hinterland but by those in the cities who, through integration over the centuries with their fellow citizens of multi-cultural nationalities, were much less likely to be impressed by 'bush medi-cines', might there be something in the story after all? And if it really *was* only fallacy, how did it achieve this reputation? One can see the connection between 'power' and the strength and rigidity of the mighty okan in the folklore of the primitive tribes, the erotic con-nection of Newtonia with its sticky sap and its strong suggestive smell, and the scientifically proven stimulatory effect of the kolanut. But the weirdly-shaped ozouga tree? Surely this has to be the ulti-mate example of fantasy triumphing over fact in man's constant flirtation with satyriasis?

*   *   *   *   *

THERE ARE OTHER 'man sticks', of course, but those four species are perhaps the most widely regarded in the West African forests as having the greatest ability to give man the 'power' he craves. Of the four, the only one able to find an enduring niche in the timber markets of Europe has been the okan. Yet okan, in my own experience, tends to be rather a loner, scattered throughout the rainforests. The ozouga is most emphatically not a loner. Ozouga forests are dense. They are invariably criss-crossed with a labyrinth of paths, many of which are of human origin, though just as many are made by elephants. The elephants are much attracted by the sweet ozouga fruit that litters the ground in a dense mass under each tree as soon as the rains are over. The green skin of the fruit turns yellow soon after it falls from the crown, like that of an over-ripe mango. This is a sign that the fruit has begun to ferment, and at this stage the smell can be quite overpowering, a sickly-sweet odour of honey. Elephants seem to be particularly attracted to it in this condition, and I have on a number of occasions watched small family groups eating it avidly. There are many stories of elephants becoming intoxicated through over-indulgence on the fermented fruit and going on drunken rampages. Though I have never personally witnesses this, I do believe that it happens. Eyewitness accounts from African hunters were too graphic and too numerous to be discarded as mere fables of the forest.

In the ozouga forests, too, I have seen what I believe to be the so-called pygmy elephant. Very few scientists give much credence to the existence of a pygmy elephant, and most believe it to be simply a small forest elephant of the ordinary species (*Loxodonta cyclotis*). The hunters of the African rainforests strongly believe the pygmy to be a quite different species. So do I. I have seen the pygmy elephant alive and I have seen the pygmy elephant dead. On one memorable occasion I attended a feast at which the main – and indeed the only – item of the menu consisted of pygmy elephant. The flesh was black and coarse, very strong to the taste and quite horrible. Hunters were unanimous in their dread of the creature, for although it stood less than two metres high at the shoulder, as compared to three metres plus for the forest elephant, it was regarded as being as irascible as the little red 'bush cow', and just as dangerous. Its tusks were smaller and thinner than those of the ordinary forest elephant, but their ivory was of the purest white and said to be much harder – and therefore more prized – than that of the larger animal.

Aggressive though it might have been when cornered, the pygmy elephant never sought the company of human beings, for it was the shyest of creatures, rarely seen by white people for it never ventured from its haunts in the deepest and darkest forests. This was quite unlike its larger relative which had not the slightest hesitation in leaving its forest habitat under cover of darkness to pillage in adjacent farm enclaves.

All elephants are fond of the ozouga fruit but they are also fond of the bark, and when they have had their fill of the fruit, they will tear great strips of it from the bole and buttresses and eat the stringy, juicy inner bark avidly. I have watched their ponderous courtship after their bellies have been filled, their prodigious S-shaped penises incredibly finding their berths without the slightest difficulty. Elephants are among the most sexually active of all the forest creatures, and they are among the very few animals of the rainforests to mate all the year round. Was this frequent mating by the mightiest of all the forest creatures the origin of the ozouga's reputation? I wonder. Maybe it was not. Maybe, in fact, it really is just a fallacy. But for we old romanticists who long to believe in the existence of the yeti, the bigfoot and the Loch Ness monster, there remains the lingering hope that some disbelieving elderly boffin in some far-off laboratory, while testing a piece of ozouga bark, will suddenly exclaim 'Eureka!' and rush outside to grab the nearest female.

As a discovery, it would certainly prove more interesting than the coelacanth.

*　　*　　*　　*　　*

IN THE EARLY part of the 1970's several hundred tons of ozouga logs were shipped from a West African port to the United States of America. In a fairly minor capacity, I had been instrumental in arranging the deal and now I watched as the ship pulled out of port. The logs had been debarked in the forest for ease of handling and to save storage space, and the logs were intended as a trial parcel for the American market.

The scheme was a failure from the word 'go'. The ultra-conservative American timber people were not much interested in top class African timbers, never mind unheard-of experimental species. The logs were left to moulder in some forgotten corner of an American port where, for all I know, they remain to this day.

Some considerable time afterwards I happened to be in California, talking to a timber magnate. It transpired that he was the entrepreneur who had purchased the shipment of ozouga. The old man had lost a lot of money on the deal and was understandably touchy on the subject, waxing long and eloquent on West African timbers in general and ozouga in particular. I tried to lighten his mood by telling him about the reputation of ozouga bark as an aphrodisiac. He stared at me. 'Maybe', he remarked wistfully, 'we should have left the bloody logs in Africa and shipped the bark to America.'

Chapter 8

Walnut and the Brimstone Tree

Botanical Name	–	*Lovoa trichilioides*
Trade Name	–	African Walnut
Other Names	–	Dibetou (Ivory Coast) Sida (Nigeria) Bombolu (Zaire)
Distribution	–	Sierra Leone to Angola.
Timber	–	Heartwood golden-bronze, with black streaks. Lustrous when planed. Works well. Tendency to split while being nailed. Glues, stains and polishes to an excellent finish.
Commercial Uses	–	Furniture, cabinet making, panelling, gunstocks, decorative veneer.

THE DENDROLOGISTS, GOD bless 'em, are quick to point out that African walnut is not a 'proper' walnut; that it is, in fact, unrelated to – and quite unlike – either the European walnut (*Juglans regia*) or the American variety (*Juglans nigra*). Even the timber barons, who, after all, named it 'African walnut' in the first place to give it better sales potential on the European markets, will concede with varying degrees of reluctance that this is indeed so.

Botanically speaking, the dendrologists are correct. True walnut belongs to the *Juglandaceae* species, while African walnut is a member of the great mahogany family of *Meliaceae*, which includes the mahoganies of the Americas and of Africa.

While no professional timbers man would have the slightest difficulty in distinguishing between European/American walnut and African walnut, it could perhaps be said that in a bad light there is a vague similarity, mainly because of the distinctive black streaking commonly found in African walnut timber and the darkly rich hue it acquires with age.

To most observers, African walnut looks a truly venerable and noble timber, even immediately after sawing and before the carpenter's plane has a chance to smooth away the rough surfaces. Indeed, for my money, it is the most beautiful of all mahogany timbers, and one which – to my admittedly biased eye – can, at its best, rival anything that the European walnut can produce.

The sapwood is narrow and of a greyish-buff hue. It rapidly becomes the playground of battalions of ambrosia beetles and therefore tends to be of little interest to the log buyer, generally being excluded from diameter measure of any logs he may purchase in the forest. The attractive black streaks found in the heartwood are caused by gum lines, and these can vary from little more than pencil-point thickness to quite broad bands of up to about ten millimetres. The grain is usually interlocked, which gives the timber a most attractive 'stripe' when quarter-sawn.

As a timber, it has most of the favourable strength properties of American black walnut, but the soft, dark glory of its coloration has long made it even more popular than this species for sliced veneers, panelling, high quality marquetry and billiard tables. It is a timber of medium density, weighing an average of 550 kg/m3, which is slightly less than the average for the other West African mahoganies. One drawback is that while it is only moderately durable, it is extremely resistant to preservatives.

Another problem can be the incidence of 'inherent grub'. This is a term beloved of West African timber men, used to describe the activities of the infamous longhorn beetle (*Cerambycidae*) which can be found all over the world, except in the polar regions and the Sahara. Just about anywhere you happen to find trees, there you will find the longhorn in one guise or another. There are more than 20,000 species of this little nuisance, and they come in all colours, from the most garish of yellows and metallic greens to the dingiest of browns and blacks. They also come in a great diversity of sizes, the largest being a chappie called *Titanus giganteus* at 15 centimetres long, excluding antennae. The adults live mainly on a diet of tree sap, plants and flowers, while the larvae eat nothing but timber, living or dead.

Most species lay their eggs in standing timber. The female bites a deep groove in the wood with her powerful jaws and lays a few eggs in it. After hatching, the grub-like larvae tunnel into the living timber, feeding on it as they proceeed. Most exist happily in this way for two to three years, eating their way steadily through the living tissue inside the tree before beginning the change from grub to adult beetle, but there are a number of tropical longhorns whose larvae can actually continue feeding in this way for anything up to 30 years before they are ready to pupate.

An enormous amount of damage can be done to the living tree by these voracious creatures during those years of eating, and the sight of grub holes on a felled log surface is usually enough to make the prospective purchaser reject that particular log out of hand.

There are certain tribes in the forests of the West African coast that regard longhorn larvae as a delicacy of the highest quality, fishing them out of their tunnels inside the log with a sliver of bamboo wherever they find them and eating them alive. I could never pluck up the courage to pop one of the large, fat, squelchy, squirming, pale-white grubs into my mouth and eat them in this fashion. However, I have tried them fried in palm oil, and found them to be an acquired taste: rather gritty, as one might have expected, and with a lingering smell of mouldering death that even the delectable palm oil could never quite conceal.

To the logger in my time, the longhorn was an unmitigated pest, and it seemed to be attracted to some tree species more than others. It certainly seemed to be especially attracted to the African walnut, and I can only assume that this was because the adults found the sap of this species particularly delectable. It was a strange fact, too, that timbers from certain areas – even countries – were more prone to attack than those from others. Timber from Liberia, for example, seemed to be sorely affected.

From my own experience, timber from the drier zones – the semi-deciduous forests – tended to be more subject to infestation. Longhorn beetles are sun-lovers, and they are less likely to be attracted to the perennial gloom of the wet evergreen forests bordering the equator. That is not to say, of course, that trees growing in those parts are completely immune from attack, but I have certainly found walnut from the lowland forests much less likely to be suffering from the depredatory assaults of those voracious creatures.

The bush carpenter was ever a pragmatist. He cared little for the aesthetic in timber. So long as a plank or a piece of wood was easy to work and did the job required of it, that was all he asked. Walnut was used no more than any other species by the ordinary forest African in any area that I was ever in, except where it happened to be particularly abundant. (In one part of the Niger Delta, it grew in such profusion that it was commonly utilized for the making of dugout canoes, a use for this species that I but rarely encountered anywhere else.) Dignitaries tended to make a little more use of its timber than the peasant: the King of Benin and the Oni of Ife, for example, adorned the walls of their palaces with plaques and masks of walnut, while a chief of the Igalas known to me had a licentious, impressively priapic 7-feet high statue carved from a walnut log in a corner of his vast living room. On one of my visits to this chief's palace I was accompanied by an impressionable young American Peace Corps girl. The startlingly life-like statue was the focus of all her attention throughout our visit, to the extent that, as we were taking leave of our host, I had the distinct feeling that she would like to have carried it off with her and left me in its place in exchange.

Much more surprising to me than the fact that there appeared to be such indifference among so many tribes about the African walnut's value as a source of timber was the fact that I so seldom found other parts of the tree favoured. Its use in medicine seemed at best minimal and, apart from the occasional juju mask, the sorcerer did not make much use of it in any tribal area that I visited.

African walnut can be a large forest tree, attaining a height of 50 metres and a diameter of 1.50 metres. The base of the tree has thick concave buttresses up to two metres high, with heavy surface roots spreading in all directions. In really favourable conditions the bole is straight, cylindrical and branchless for the first 25 metres. The crown itself is heavily branched and dome-like, though not massive in relation to the size of the tree, and it is quite dark in silhouette against the clear sky. The bark is dark grey and scaly on older trees, and the deeply pink slash has a most beautiful cedar-like scent.

The tree inhabits a variety of sites. I have come across African walnut growing in the wetter parts of the evergreen rain-forest and also in the higher parts of northern Liberia's Nimba Range at around 800 metres above sea level. Trees growing at such altitudes and in shallow rocky soils tend to be squat and sturdy of bole, rather than of the tall and graceful form one expects to find in the deep humid soils of the lowlands. In such abnormal conditions, the trees are often much more heavily buttressed. Far greater concentrations can be found in the rainforest proper, but, as seed fertility with walnut has always been traditionally good, and the single seeds are equipped with a large wing on the tail – like a horizontal propeller – they could be carried far from the parent tree in the wind. Hill slopes are thus often a favourite catchment area for them, regardless of suitability of growing conditions.

It is, therefore, in the lowland forests that African walnut can be seen growing at its best. In such areas, where you find one, you will often find plenty more. It can be gregarious in conditions that suit it, but, although it is fond of heavy rainfall, it does not like swamp or even periodically inundated areas. In the Niger Delta of my day it could quite commonly be found in patches of forest loosely termed 'swamp forest', but only on the better drained soils within those areas. Here, too, it often shares sites with another lover of dark and wet places, the brimstone tree.

The *Nauclea* genus, to which the brimstone belongs, has representatives in a wide range of habitats and climatic conditions in Africa. The splendidly named *Nauclea vanderguchtii*, for example, is quite a large and handsome tree that often grows in swamp forests in association with abura (*Mitragyna ciliata*). Others of the genus even grow in savannah country, and they are usually warty little shrubs no bigger than apple trees. The only member of the *Nauclea* genus of the slightest interest to the timber man today is the brimstone tree, or *Nauclea diderrichii* – better known as kusia, opepe or bilinga, depending where in West Africa it happens to be growing. This is a heavy-density timber tree whose popularity has been escalating dramatically since the Second World War.

It is a large and spectacular tree, reaching 50 metres in height and 1.50 metres in diameter, with a straight and cylindrical bole and large bottle-green, aspen-shaped leaves. The timber is golden-yellow when fresh-felled, turning gradually to a lustrous yellow-brown on exposure. It has exceptional strength properties and a very high resistance to termite and fungal attack. Much favoured by the boat-building trade throughout Europe, it is also extensively used for flooring, furniture, piling and general construction.

The people of the delta regions along the Gulf of Guinea made their canoes from brimstone and, because of its durability and the ease with which it could be worked with primitive tools, most of their rice mortars. Many Liberian tribes, in fact, called this tree 'mortar-stick'.

The brimstone tree had many uses in medicine, too, decoctions of bark and leaves acting as antidotes for just about everything from measles to snakebite. In some ports along the Coast pieces of root were boiled in water and the solution drunk daily by those free-spirited young ladies whose lifestyles necessitated close association with such peripatetic and high-spending sailors as happened to come their way, in the generally vain hope that the brimstone solution would ward off the embarrassing ailments that were the occupational hazard of such fleeting amatory engagements. One could easily scorn naive faith in such essentially 'native' treatments, but, as a medical friend of mine wisely remarked to me many years ago, it was not so very long ago that we 'civilized' races were extolling the virtues of sulphur baths for much the same reason.

Dark and gloomy forests were where the walnut and the brimstone seemed to me to be most at home. Here, too, could frequently be found two other – much smaller – species of tree.

The butter tree (*Pentadesma butyracea*), was virtually useless as timber even for such primitive carpentry as might have been required by the villagers of the interior, so coarse and stringy was the wood. In fact, the only interesting thing about this tree is its fruit – great, pendulous, dark-green globes about 15 centimetres long by 10 centimetres wide, full of yellow, fatty pulp. Some tribes would mix the pulp with stews, while others would make a sort of bush soap from the oil-rich seeds. In some parts of Liberia, a country whose unfortunate people have, over the last few decades, had ample cause to be suspicious of their neighbours, the fruit is still eaten as a preventative against poisoning by those journeying to a strange part of the country. Needless to say, the squishy fruits are soon eaten by elephants, chimpanzees and wild pigs when they fall to the ground.

An even greater lover of shady places than the walnut and the brimstone once found in abundance in those wet lowland forests is the aptly-named 'yellow-wood', or *Enantia polycarpa*. Although the yellow-wood could attain a height of some 8 metres and perhaps 0.3 of a metre in diameter, it would more typically be encountered as a tall and straight understorey stick of a thing of no more than wrist thickness, its dark-green bark making it inconspicuous in the gloom of the forest. But it was, nevertheless, a most remarkable 'stick', because of the many uses to which the forest indigène put it.

Yellow-wood is a beautiful little tree under its unassuming cloak. Take a slice from its skin-thin outer bark and two things will strike you simultaneously – the incredibly beautiful golden-yellow of its inner bark, almost fluoresecent in such dim light, and the gloriously heady fragrance that wafts over you from the exposed cambium in a soft invisible cloud. Its timber does not disappoint either, what little there is of it. Of the brightest, clearest yellow, yet with the most delicate tinge of green to it, the wood is light in weight and has a satiny lustre, but it is very tough and quite durable. When the light hits it at an appropriate angle, the wood takes on a most attractive silvery sheen, and a fine glossy finish adds to its lustre.

This is one tree of which in the past the forest African made extensive use. In some areas it was referred to as 'the chief's tree', and the houses of chiefs would often be timbered with this species, especially rafters, door posts, lintels, verandahs, beds, tables. Ceremonial caps were made from the fragrant, fibrous bark, and a yellow dye was produced from both the wood and the inner bark. Skin infections were treated with an infusion from bark and roots, and the fruit – strange, reddish-black, finger-like things that projected most conspicuously in bunches from a common axis on the twig – would often adorn the huts of witchdoctors during important fertility festivals, in much the same way as mistletoe is hung in houses at Christmas in more advanced societies even today.

In fact, such is the attractiveness of this remarkable little tree that only its modest size has saved it from the attentions of the logger. As it is, it will probably vanish in the end, for it is completely dependent upon the permanent shade afforded by its lofty neighbours. When they go, as go they must, this lovely tree will undoubtedly perish with them.

*   *   *   *   *

I WAS STANDING IN a West African sawmill, watching the sawyers manhandling a huge walnut butt through the headrig. It had obviously been part of a tree that had experienced some of life's less tranquil moments, for it was a gnarled and lumpy old brute of a thing, grossly scaly of bark, with a huge burl on one side of it and a wide and ancient lightning scar marking it from end to end.

An hour later the log had been reduced to large baulks of timber, ten feet long by three feet wide and three inches thick. Whether the lightning strike had disturbed its metabolism in some mysterious way, or it had been growing in singularly unsuitable terrain, the grain and the timber colours were quite unlike anything I had ever seen in African walnut before. Instead of the more normal reasonably regular stripes of gold and bronze interspersed with thin black lines, the planks before me were patterned from one end to the other with most un-walnut-like tangled whorls and great moiré washes of bronze and green and copper and chocolate, with – through the centre of each plank – a ten-inch broad band of the deepest black.

The mill owner was not a happy man. There was obviously little of the artist in his make-up. He was, first and foremost, a technical man. This log, he groused, was not true walnut. This was a freak of nature, and these planks from it were decidedly freakish, too. He would never be able to sell them at a profit, he told me. He made up his mind there and then that he had no option but to reduce them to run-of-the-mill lumber and sell the parcel off locally at whatever price he could get for them. I easily persuaded him to let me have one of the huge planks in its original state, gratis.

Osei the Carpenter was a friend of mine. He was also the best African carpenter I have ever known, and I have known a few good ones. He was a man with a genuine love of timber and of his work, and he took pride in producing only the best. I gave him the plank and told him that I wanted a long centre table for my living room from it. Make me a table so good that I shall be able to boast to my friends ever after that this is the finest work of Osei the Carpenter, I told him, and ten whole American dollars would be his for his efforts.

It was the best ten dollars I have ever spent. The Carpenter worked and whittled and smoothed and polished at that plank for a month. He put no artificial substances on it, but by the end of that month the surface had a lustre that would have dazzled you in the noonday sun. Copper and viridian and carmine and chocolate and darkly violet whorls and broad wavy bands of old-gold glowed and sparkled on this beautiful piece of timber from end to end. Down the centre of the table, there was a ten-inches-wide band of the blackest of blacks, a black that shone like obsidian.

It was quite the finest piece of timber I have ever seen. As for Osei the Carpenter, well, he had two wives and seventeen children, most of them his. He was reasonably fond of all of them, but none gave him so much pleasure as did that new table he had made to me. On occasion, when he would find the exuberant proximity of his family beginning to gnaw at his nerve ends, he would down tools and escape to my bachelor house for a beer. We would sit together mostly in silence, as really good friends ought to be able to do, just communicating without feeling that there was any social obligation to disturb our thoughts with vulgar speech. His gaze would inevitably drift to the centre table, moving slowly over it, back and forth, back and forth, basking in the warmth and the wonder of it. Then he would sigh deeply and wonder aloud why Allah – for Osei had been a recent convert to the Islamic faith – should have concentrated so much of His Heavenly quota of beauty in the making of a tree and yet have put so little of it into the making of the human race.

My friend was subject to periodic depressions, as I suppose any man with two wives and seventeen children has every right to be at times. He was also a bit of a philosopher. But the Carpenter was wrong on this one. Allah supplies the material, all right, but it is man who messes that material around, generally with catastrophic results.

Allah was probably subject to fits of depression, too, at what He was witnessing down below Him on earth. But He must surely have been tickled pink by what Osei the Carpenter did with the raw material He had given him to work with in the form of timbers from the great trees of Africa's rainforests.

Osei's afterlife is secure. Even in an Islamic Heaven, there is surely a place for one more good Carpenter.

Chapter 9

The Khaya Kings

Botanical Name	–	*Khaya ivorensis*
Trade Name	–	Khaya or African Mahogany
Other Names	–	Oganwo and lagoswood (Nigeria) Ngollon and acajou (Cameroon)
Distribution	–	The West African rainforests
Timber	–	Delicate pink when fresh felled, darkening to a mellow reddish brown. Interlocked grain. Fairly easy to work and takes an excellent finish.
Commercial Uses	–	Furniture and cabinet making, boat-building, interior joinery, decorative veneers.

On the Mahogany Trail

IN THE APPEARANCE and working properties of its timbers, the *Khaya* genus of Africa comes closest to the true mahoganies of the Caribbean and South America.

Although there are four species of Khaya within West Africa, only *K. ivorensis* grows in the rainforest proper, while others tend to favour the rather drier conditions flanking the more northerly parts of the rainforest belt. *K. senegalensis*, a much smaller and more misshapen tree than the others, is to be found only in pockets of deciduous woodland between the northern perimeter of the rainforests and the beginnings of the arid desert zone.

Timbers are quite variable within the Khayas, however, as might be expected through the considerable variations in climatic and geographical conditions in which they grow. Most in demand on the European market has always been that of the lagoswood, or *Khaya ivorensis*. Because of their darker and denser nature, beninwood and savannah mahogany are rather less attractive to the exporters. From my own personal experience, an additional drawback with beninwood has always been the fact that the living tree tends to be prone to attack by the larvae of the longhorn beetle, especially among those trees growing at the northerly limit of its range in the small pockets of semi-deciduous forest scattered throughout the moister patches of ground among the elephant grass of the fringing savannah. However, the timber from the fourth member of the genus, acajou-blanc (*K. anthotheca*), while much plainer in appearance and of slightly coarser texture than lagoswood, has often been used in recent years to adulterate shipments when exporters in some countries have encountered a shortfall in the immediate supply of lagoswood. Few notice the difference at the other end.

As with the true mahoganies of the Americas, there can be considerable variations of mahogany hue in the timbers of the African variety. Again, local topography as well as soil and climatic conditions appear to be contributory factors. The lighter – and more desirable – shades of red/brown come from the wetter evergreen coastal forests where the true African mahogany (*K. ivorensis*) is predominant, while in the drier forests to the north coloration becomes appreciably darker. Savannah mahogany is so dark as to have a decidedly purplish tinge to it.

The word 'mahogany' is one that continues to puzzle the linguists. There have been a number of theories floated as to its possible derivation. The most plausible – to me, at least – would seem to be that it had its origins in the slave trade. 'Oganwo' is the Yoruba name for African mahogany, while the Portuguese name for the Swietenias of South America was 'mogno'. When slaves from Nigeria arrived in the forests of Brazil, they instantly spotted the strong resemblance the Swietenias had to the Khayas of their own land. Thus, by the combining of 'mogno' and 'oganwo' in conversation for the benefit of both themselves and their new masters, the slaves gave us 'mahogany', a word that, ironically, came to be applied to the oganwo of their own distant land with the passage of time.

Wherever the word came from, there can no doubt that little difference separates the timbers of the two genera. Indeed, a comparison study from any major timber book will show there to be a remarkable similarity under all the standard headings of weight, general description, mechanical properties, seasoning properties, working properties and durability. Even under the heading of 'uses', the only technical differences would appear to be that the greater variations in figuring found in the wood of the Swietenias – fiddleback, blister, roe, pommelle, and so forth – meant that the mahoganies of the Caribbean and South America always tended to be the snob's choice in the rarified atmosphere of the more up-market sections of the furniture trade.

Tradition, of course, has also had its part to play in this, as in every other trade. The African mahoganies, as a consequence, have always tended to be regarded as the poor relation. This is understandable. If one may use a rather weak analogy, Scotch whisky might, after all, be just as easy to make in parts of England, and it might even – but whisper this in the presence of Scotsmen – be just as good as anything produced north of the border. However, no connoisseur in his right mind would think of buying the English variety (and certainly not at the same price) while the 'real' thing is available.

Frankly, I am biased in favour of Africa. There has always seemed to me to be a sort of mellowness about Africa's oganwo, the mellowness that does not fit so comfortably with descriptions of the timbers from its more famous counterpart across the water. It is the sort of mellowness you get with, say, a good Islay malt as compared to the dark and exotic fruitiness of the wines of Old Oporto, if one may be allowed to strain the analogy to breaking point. I suppose it is a matter of taste: the traditionalists prefer the rather sombre and dignified splendour of the Swietenias, while the cheerful, almost golden aura that seems always to emanate from the African equivalent finds greater favour with those modernists to whom tradition is not everything. And, of course, to all we 'Old Coasters' who have fond memories of this lovely tree.

I have encountered its timber in use wherever I have travelled: as banister rails in shopping malls from Glasgow to Tulsa; as furnishing in the homes and play-palaces of the Hollywood jet-set from the San Bernando Valley to the casinos of Las Vegas. The rather beat-up old piano in the corner of a Bronx honky-tonk in which I once found myself was made of oganwo, as were the shelves of a plush college library in St John's, Newfoundland, where I worked for a time. The toilet seats in a shabby Lebanese home I occasionally visited were made from oganwo, as were the rough flooring planks of the living quarters. Its uses are many and it is reasonably durable. The boat building trade makes much use of it, particularly in yachts and the furnishing of luxury liners.

In the Africa of my day, oganwo was occasionally used for the making of dugout canoes, but more often than not fallen trees would be pitsawn into planks for house construction. It is a tree that floats easily, and a common sight on any one of the calm, winding waterways of the Niger Delta of half a century ago would be the long narrow rafts of mahogany logs being poled on their ways to the shipping points of the Coast. Log poachers were a common hazard: the Ijaw tribesmen could swim like seals and they would slip through the water under cover of darkness, slice through the ropes binding the logs together, then push the log or logs before them through the water to some prearranged point among the concealing mangroves. A week or so later, identifying scribe marks carefully whittled away from the wood surfaces with adzes, the logs would be sold by the poachers, often back to the company from which they had been stolen in the first place. The log exporters ranted and swore, but in the end they always paid up: they were generally only too happy to get the logs back one way or another. Some rafting contractors even became so sophisticated as to run their own little extortion rackets. Pay those black Al Capones a good deal over the odds for transporting your logs from A to B and you were guaranteed safe passage for them.

It was a lucrative business, and for a time I had the dubious distinction of being on reasonably friendly terms with an eminent cabinet minister from a large Third World country whose meteoric rise to the top in government had been greatly assisted by the considerable largesse accumulated during his formative years when he had been a successful and aggressive log thief in the coastal waters of his native land.

The first felled tree I ever saw in Africa was that of the oganwo, or, more specifically, *Khaya ivorensis*. In fact, it was not just one of them that lay before my eyes at that moment – there must have been fifty of them there, side by side, in a timber landing in the heart of the Sapoba forests of southern Nigeria. They were being processed in preparation for loading on to trucks for the short journey down to the waterside, where they would be made into rafts for transportation to Sapele, Nigeria's main timber port in those days. The long boles were being crosscut into predetermined lengths and the bark was being removed from them by teams of workers. The scent from both bark and sawdust filled the air with the sweetest of fragrances, a fragrance so heady as to make one almost forget the stench of diesel fumes that came from the massive lorries lined up at the entrance to the clearing and the monstrous Skagit loading winch under the lofty spar tree out in the centre. The fresh pinkness of the new log surfaces was quite the prettiest shade of pink I had ever seen – so extraordinarily refined as to make one almost think of it, too, as being a fragrance rather than a colour. The sweat glistened in a mother-of-pearl sheen in the morning sun on sinewy black bodies as they wielded axes and adzes all around me. It is a sight that remains with me now, as vivid as when I saw it then, and it is the most beautiful of memories. It is also a memory tinged with sadness, for, with the sort of sagacity that can generally only be acquired with the hindsight of the elderly, I realise only too well that what I was watching then was the demise of the most colourful and vibrant and wonderful tropical rainforest this world has ever seen, and that I had had a hand in its destruction.

This oganwo is a tall tree, reaching about 50 metres in height and with a dark grey, rather scaly bark. Because of its height, it gives the impression at first sight of being rather a slender tree, although its bole can reach diameters of around 1.30 metres. The tiny white flowers, crowded at the ends of the branchlets during each dry season, produce masses of small brown-winged seeds enclosed in large woody pods which, when fully opened, can be plainly seen from the ground as they stand out, star-shaped, against the green of the crown or the blue of the sky.

Most tree books describe the bole as being almost completely straight for most of its length, but I have rarely found this to be so. In my experience, it can often be beautifully straight for the first quarter of its length, then becoming increasingly sinuous towards the crown. Logs are generally cylindrical, but the larger diameters – especially from trees growing in fairly dry locations – tended often to be affected by brittle or spongy heartwood and cross-fractures, particularly in logs from the first 10 metres of bole length.

Traditionally, the best oganwo was always to be found in the humid evergreen forests bordering the West African coastline and deep into the forests of equatorial Cameroon. But it is not a swamp tree. Although it does grow best in proximity to water, it has to be running water, and it is to be seen at its optimum growth when found on the banks of streams and rivers. Many other species could be found in loose association with it in these fertile grounds. The agba (*Gossweilerodendron balsamiferum*), a tree whose splendid scientific name is in keeping with its magnificent appearance, is a simply colossal tree of the most perfectly cylindrical shape of possibly any forest tree in the world. It has no buttresses or even root swellings, but seems to have been planted where it stands, like some Brobdingnagian telephone pole, and its bole is virtually without blemish of any kind. Its timber is of a rather undistinguished light tan hue, and it is full of a dark treacly oleoresin. I have watched workers setting buckets under newly crosscut logs to catch the resin oozing from them, to use as lighting fuel in their huts and for a variety of tribal medicines. In the early days, before sophisticated modern technology eased the problem somewhat, this gum could be a horrible nuisance through clogging up the saws, but today agba is popular in Europe for many purposes where mechanical strength properties in timber is not so important. Selected logs are even sliced for veneers.

Once a very common tree found in those same evergreen forests, the afina (*Strombosia spp.*) is no forest giant; it is a tall, skinny understorey tree which, at best, can attain a height of 30 metres, but rarely diameters exceeding 50 centimetres. It is straight but rather knobbly of stem, and quite without branches up to the very small, dense, dull-green crown. The bark is dark-grey, but as it is of a very scaly habit and the scales soon fall off to leave yellow, green, orange and brown scars, the overall appearance is that of a tree which has been painted in camouflage shades by the military services, with even the anonymous dusty green of the leaves enhancing that impression. The timber is one of the hardest and heaviest in Africa – about 1,000 kg/m3 – and it is most attractive, being of a pale purplish-tan hue with darker purple streaks running through it. The wood is lustrous, fine-textured, straight-grained, durable, tough and strong, and were it not for the tree's small size, this is one species that would undoubtedly have made it on the export market long ago. In fact, it did briefly find favour as a flooring timber in the dance halls of Europe during the 1930's. It is one of the very few timbers in the world that wears smoothly, like marble, under heavy foot traffic, rather than splintering – but the trade did not survive the war years. I have myself used it for telegraph poles in Africa. Locally, it is a popular house-building tree and, in the old days, decoctions from bark and roots were used for making ointments to treat lepers and those with withered hands and feet.

I don't know what the oganwo forests of the Coast are like today, if indeed they exist at all. But in my day they were full of life. Fish eagles patrolled the skies and the melodic calls of the handsome, rufous-backed mona monkeys resounded in diminuendo through the treetops. Snow-white egrets, scarlet-and-black weavers and turquoise-and-white kingfishers flashed and shimmered and fluttered amidst the floral beauty of the deltas. Many and weird were the creatures that inhabited this region of such primitive beauty, but possibly the strangest of all was to be found, not above the surface of the water, but in it. This was the West African mantee.

It is widely believed today that the myth of the mermaid had its origins in this peculiar animal. If this be so, then all I can say is that the sailors who first spread this tale must have had their minds addled by too much bad grog or a dearth of willing cabin boys, for the manatee is surely one of the most unprepossessing of all of God's creations. It is dark-grey, three metres long, and a shapeless mass of blubber with a squashed face and a bristly moustache. The male is even uglier. A sailor would need to be shipwrecked on his own for a very long time before succumbing to erotic fantasies about the West African manatee.

Although it has much the same shape and appearance as a seal, the manatee is rarely seen. It never comes out of the water, although occasionally you might see its head pop above the surface to peer shortsightedly at your canoe as you pass by on the river. It dwells in the salty, brackish and fresh coastal waters of West Africa, travelling far up any river that takes its fancy, such as the Niger, living on a diet of seaweed, freshwater plants, and the pernicious water hyacinth.

Manatees are gentle creatures, with a few of the more endearing characteristics of the human race and none of the less attractive ones. Their courtship is a langorous affair: they embrace and cuddle up to one another, and they mate belly to belly underwater. The young (usually only one) are breast-fed, and this phase can last for up to two years. The mother has two teats, which probably helps to perpetuate the myth of the mermaid. The youngster often hitches a ride on its mother's back as she moves from place to place.

I have seen the manatee often, though usually when dead as a result of a fisherman's spear. I have also eaten manatee, but not with much enthusiasm, although the flesh is undoubtedly good and it is much sought for this reason. Fortunately, this completely harmless creature is now given a certain amount of protection in some areas, but it will always be hunted wherever there is a need to feed hungry children in remote areas, regardless of any legislation to protect it. This is yet another species that will almost certainly become extinct during the next half century.

*   *   *   *   *

A COUPLE OF YEARS ago I was walking along a path on the outskirts of a small English town when a lorry loaded with logs passed by. Something about the logs looked familiar, and the shipping mark clearly visible on the end of the one nearest to me as the lorry trundled past I certainly recognised. A short distance down the road the truck turned into a timber yard.

A week later, chance took me into the same yard. I introduced myself to the owner and mentioned the load I had seen entering his premises. 'Yes,' he said, 'you're right. African mahogany. They came into Felixstowe a fortnight ago. We buy the occasional parcel.'

I watched while his workers crosscut the ends off the logs. The scent of the oganwo wafted faintly to my nostrils, still recognizable, for it was still not too many years since I had stood in an African timber landing. But the fragrance did not have either the strength or the poignancy that I remembered. There was a sort of mustiness about it, a death smell, the sort of smell you get from anything that has been crammed in the hold of a vessel for so long that it has become nothing more than an item on the ship's manifest. Something else was missing, too. And then it came to me. It was the bush that was missing. The smells and sights and sounds of the African bush: the hotness; the cloying, boiling humidity; the workers, sweating and singing as they toiled; the parrots wheeling and calling overhead against the blue cloudless skies of ancient Africa.

My Africa. There was nothing in the whole of England that could replace that.

Chapter 10

The Big and the Beautiful

Botanical Name — *Entandrophragma cylindricum*

Trade Name — Sapele

Other Names — Aboudikro (Ivory Coast)
Sapelewood (Nigeria)
Sapelli (Cameroon)

Distribution — The African rainforests

Timber — Pink when fresh-felled, soon darkening to a typical mahogany reddish-brown. Marked and regular stripe; occasional mottle figure. Works well with all tools but interlocked grain can give difficulty in planing. Excellent finish.

Commercial Uses — Decorative veneer, furniture, boat-building, panelling.

BIG IS BEAUTIFUL, assert my sapient young female friends as they slap the war paint on in preparation for yet another reconnaissance of the talent at the local night club. They should know, I suppose, for this is a superficial and materialistic age. But who am I to quarrel with them? I have lived among the big and the beautiful for a very large part of my life.

Nothing in the world of tropical trees was bigger and more beautiful than those representatives of Africa's very own *Entandrophragma* genus to be found in the rainforests of the White Man's Grave in my day. For sheer enormity, for towering length and cylindrical perfection of bole, those trees were supreme. A forest full of these giants was as impressive and awe-inspiring a sight as this world has ever seen. It is a sadness to me today that nowhere in all of Africa will one now find them in the sizes that I did then, great serried ranks of them, mile after mile after mile of them, God's very own plantation of mahoganies, standing like massive pillars from some long-gone Greek or Roman city. I have no doubt the Entandrophragmas are still there today, but even in the very much reduced sizes they are available now, you will never encounter them in the quantities I remember, and mankind will never do so again. The logger, the subsistence farmer, the corrupt politics of Third World governments and third rate timber companies have ensured that we shall not.

For a long time it was the very enormity of many of the individual trees of this genus that was to save their collective bacon. In its green state it was never a difficult tree to fell by axe, for its timber was surprisingly easy to cut, and when the day of the chainsaw arrived in the late 1950's, the fate of even the largest of those forest goliaths should have been well and truly sealed. The problems, of course, came not in the actual felling, but they were problems that had exercised the minds of timber operatives ever since logging began on the Coast: how to handle them once they had been felled. It was a situation common to a few individuals of other species, of course, but with the Entandrophragmas it was particularly exasperating, for often the best figuring – and therefore the timber commanding the highest prices in European markets – was to be found in the older and larger logs. I have seen these trees three metres in diameter, and two metres diameter was by no means uncommon. Loggers possessed neither the means to haul logs of this size from stump to loading point in those early days nor yet anything capable of transporting them either to shipping port or point of manufacture. Nor would monsters of these dimensions be welcome in many plymills or sawmills then, even in the most modern and sophisticated of factories.

All this had changed by the 1970's with the introduction of modern machinery capable of handling almost anything that Mother Nature could produce, with the result that, like most of the other prized timber species, the Entandrophragmas of West Africa have now become an endangered species. Although strictly African, it is a genus closely related to the Swietenias, the true mahoganies of the Americas. Of eight species, only four are to be found within the forests of West Africa. The timbers of the Entandrophragmas and the Swietenias are not only remarkably similar in appearance, but in most respects they are also comparable in properties and quality, particularly the esteemed sapele (*Entandrophragma cylindricum*).

West Africa's *Entandrophragma* representatives are:

> *E. angolense*   (tiama or gedunohor)
> *E. candollei*   (kosipo or omu)
> *E. cylindricum*   (sapele or aboudikro)
> *E. utile*   (sipo or utile)

Sapele and sipo are by far the most sought for the quality of their timber and, indeed, the uses to which their respective timbers are put are virtually identical. The more decorative of the two – and therefore the most expensive – is sapele, with its characteristically beautiful and regular thin stripe when sawn on the quarter, as compared to the much broader and rather coarsely irregular ribbon stripe of sipo. The timber of sapele also diffuses a most delectable cedar-scent – a scent that remains with it long after the wood has been processed into the finished article – as distinct from that of sipo, which seldom has any kind of fragrance to it.

In contrast to the timbers of sapele and sipo, that of kosipo appears almost funereal, even to the extent of developing a darkly tenebrous, purplish tinge on exposure, and, while a ribbon-figure is sometimes visible on quarter-sawn surfaces, almost never will one find it to have the attractive striping that is the hallmark of sapele. Kosipo timber has the added disadvantage of being much coarser of grain than that of either sapele, sipo or tiama, and it often contains small silica granules in its rays. All those defects, plus a tendency to distort badly on drying, have made it decidedly less popular with the timber trade than the others. Its uses have generally been restricted to items of high-class carpentry and various types of naval construction. I even have a memory of it being used as carriage panelling on the London, Midland and Scottish Railway in my youth. It does, however, produce quite good veneer, occasionally with an attractive moiré figuring.

While they are quite easy to work with hand tools when the trees are newly felled, there is no doubt that the timbers of both sapele and sipo – in common with all the mahoganies – become hard and rather difficult to work with hand tools when they have dried out. Bush carpenters therefore tended not to waste much time on them with chisel and plane when in this condition. The occasional tree, either felled illegally or flattened by wind, would be pitsawn into planks for building purposes soon after it had fallen, but that would be about it. Only in the homes of chiefs and in the palaces of kings would highly polished furniture and artifacts of those species be found. For ordinary mortals, plenty of other species were much easier to work and rarely needed a lot of smoothing and shaping for the mundane domestic products normally required.

In any case, by the beginning of the 1950's prices for sapele had begun to escalate. Unwin reports that in the 1930's canoes were regularly made from this species – indeed, he writes of seeing a canoe over 80 feet long with a draught of more than 6 feet made from sapelewood – but I cannot remember seeing anything like this. By the 1950's tribal chiefs had learned that far greater rewards were on offer through the sale of individual logs to itinerate timber merchants than were to be gained from utilizing them to satisfy personal vanities and maintaining status with their tribesmen. Already, the Great White God, Denarius, had begun to dismember the traditional values of the coastal tribes with his grasping claws.

Sapele timber has a lot going for it. Of all the so-called 'mahoganies' – African, American or Caribbean – it is my favourite by a wide margin. It takes the most glorious polish of any timber I have ever known, a rich, warm glow that goes straight to the heart. There is also the sheer beauty of its incredible figuring. Sapele has always been famed for its 'stripey' figure, but sometimes much more complex patterns will suddenly blossom before your eyes on sawing, to the gratified surprise of the chap who purchased the log in the first place. These patterns may appear as mottlings, ripples, whorls, moiré waves or in a sort of 'partridge-wing' type of figure. Whichever they may be, they invariably add enormously to the value of the timber. In my own experience, the more exotic of these configurations are almost always encountered in the butt log of the tree and very rarely in the main stem. (In the same way as the most prized timber from the European walnut, *Juglans regia*, is to be found in the base of the tree and in its main roots.) Indeed, I recall one colossal sapele tree which had been felled by a farmer wishing to clear his land for cocoa in the Ondo Province of Nigeria. It was a very old tree which, from the ancient scar tissue and the myriad corrugations on its blunt and heavy buttresses, had obviously suffered considerably over the ages from the effects of fire. Some entrepreneurial young forestry assistants – of which number I confess to having been one – decided that it would be a good idea to have the whole stump dug up and pitsawn by a local contractor. The resultant planks produced the most incredibly lovely examples of 'bird's eye' figuring I have ever seen in my life. The fact that the logging company by whom we were all employed was never made aware of this acquisitive action on land that was, after all, part of their own legal timber concession, was no doubt shameful. However, the fact remains that in due course all those planks were converted into the most beautiful of boxes – trinket, jewellery and cigar containers – by the hands of a bush carpenter renowned for his skill at making such things. There are a lot of jewellery boxes in two tons of figured sapele and it was a long time before any of us had to think again about buying Christmas presents for our nearest and dearest.

All the Entandrophragmas are imposing forest giants, often growing to a height of 50 to 60 metres, and at those heights they are truly massive in girth. They all tend to have a rather scattered habitat, but there can be exceptions to this general rule. I have seen large stands of sipo in southern Nigeria and Liberia and of sapele in the depths of the rainforests of southern Cameroon, while the rocky terrain of the Ikeji-Ipetu forest of Ondo Province in Nigeria consisted almost entirely of the highest quality sapele at one time. In my own experience, the greater concentrations of the species tended to be in the drier, deeper and better-drained soils along the northern flanks of the evergreen forests of the Coast, and it was in this sort of terrain that the bigger trees could be found. In general, much smaller girths and much fewer concentrations of individual species tended to be found within the limits of the true rainforests.

The different species of Entandrophragma found in West Africa are, to the layman, remarkably alike in appearance in that they are of such striking sizes and with such perfectly cylindrical boles, and their crowns are always similarly dome-shaped and heavily branched. However, a closer inspection of the standing trees will reveal certain differences and these are worth recording here.

Sipo can have heavy buttresses up to 3 metres high, while sapele, though it may have buttresses up to 2 metres high when growing on a hillside, is more generally to be found with heavy root swellings only. Kosipo rarely has buttresses, although it often carries heavy root swellings.

On mature trees, sapele bark is of a brownish-ochre hue, with irregular scales which leave distinct mussel-shell markings when shed. Sipo bark is a very distinctive silvery-grey, is deeply grooved vertically, and has large longitudinal, rectangular scales. Kosipo bark is of a depressingly dark-greyish-to-mocha scumble, with round irregular scales which fall off and leave distinctive pits on the surface of the bark, like smallpox scars.

The slash of both sapele and sipo is fibrous and pink, but sapele slash is strongly fragrant while the sipo has little, if any, fragrance.

Kosipo slash is brownish-pink, very granular, with bright-orange stone inclusions in its cells, and it is not in the slightest fragrant.

A curious and most pleasing characteristic of sapele is that when the sun's rays rest on the bark of the standing tree, its cedar fragrance is released to linger strongly and persistently all around it.

Sapele, sipo and kosipo all regenerate by winged seeds which are contained in long, spindle-shaped capsules from which – assuming that the capsule bothers to open at all – the seeds whirl slowly and lethargically to the forest floor. Being high in fat content, most are soon eaten by insects and animals. God alone knows how any survive, but obviously a tiny proportion do so for regeneration of seedlings under the parent tree can be quite prolific until, inevitably, they get smothered by faster growing vegetation or eaten by duikers.

Another of the great tropical family of Meliaceae to which the mahoganies belong is the Guarea genus. The two main timber species of this genus found in West Africa are *Guarea cedrata* and *G. thompsonii*. They can be found scattered throughout the semi-deciduous zones of the Coast and – just occasionally – in the wetter forests bordering the coastal swamps. They are, however, to be seen at their best in conditions particularly favoured by the Entandrophragmas – deep well-drained soils immediately to the north of areas of optimum rainfall.

The Guareas of both species are splendid looking trees and, like the Entandrophragmas, have long been in favour with the timber trade. (Unwin reports that a member of the genus – presumably *G. cedrata* – was sold as 'scented mahogany' on the Liverpool market in 1906 at 3½d to 3¾d per superficial foot.) Generally speaking, *G. cedrata* – marketed variously as bossé, white guarea and scented guarea – has been more popular, partly due to its strong fragrance of cedar and partly because it has less tendency to split and warp on drying than *G. thompsonii* or 'black guarea'. However, all other working properties are so similar and favourable that one often finds them lumped together for such purposes as carpentry and furniture making, although bossé, by tradition, has always been the one used in the making of instrument boxes and cigar boxes.

Guarea timber is of a pinkish-brown hue when the tree is fresh-felled, darkening slowly to an attractive silky, pale-brown on exposure, much more identifiable with the true cedar (*Cedrus sp.*) of Mediterranean and Himalayan countries and the 'pseudo-cedars' such as pencil-cedar (*Juniperus virginiana*) and Thuya from North America than with any of the Swietenias or the Entandrophragmas. Guarea's impact on the export markets would have been even greater were it not for its annoying tendency to exude resin even after it has supposedly been kiln dried. The timber is light, easy to saw, it takes paint varnishes well, and it can be made into excellent plywood and veneer.

Guarea is a large and handsome tree, both species attaining a height of 40 metres or more and a diameter of 1.5 metres in favourable conditions. It has very thin, tall, concave buttresses which spread in all directions around the tree. The bark of mature trees is most distinctive, with large oblong scales that drop off when dry to leave 'mussel-shell' pittings which contain within them concentric ridges. There is a distinct differences in bark colour between the two species, that of *G. cedrata* being a pale greyish-yellow colour while the bark of *G. thompsonii* is a dark brown colour with a purplish wash intermingled with it in mature trees.

Common wherever the Entandrophragmas and the Guareas grow is another member of the Meliaceae genus, the 'Devil-Mask Tree' (*Trichilia heudelotii*), which is no forest giant. On the contrary, it is a skinny understorey tree, never much more than 15 metres tall. It is worth a mention, though, for before the arrival of the white man in the domain of the African forest the Devil-Mask Tree was of considerably more importance to the people of the forest than any mahogany that ever lived. As its native name indicates, this was mainly the tree from which juju masks were made for festivals and ceremonies involving witchcraft. The lustrous reddish-brown heart-wood was extremely durable but surprisingly light. It was easily worked with even the crudest of tools and it did not crack on drying, which made it ideal not only for the making of masks but also for the carving of the many other fetishes and charms that were part and parcel of every self-respecting witchdoctor's trade. Indeed, its working properties were so favourable that it would long ago have joined the list of species required by the log exporters were it not for the fact that here was a tree that simply did not grow to the girth required by the export trade.

The flowers of the Devil Mask Tree are tiny, light-olive, and fragrant. The resultant fruits, though small (about 10mm in diameter), are among the most conspicuously beautiful in the whole of the African rainforests, the scarlet aril of each fruit half-covering numerous very small shiny black seeds.

Another common understorey family of trees much in evidence is the one which produces both the ebony timber of commerce and the fruit of the American persimmon. This is the *Ebenaceae*, of which the genus *Diospyrus* is by far the most important from a timber point of view. Although much of the export quality African ebony comes from a relatively small number of species (two of the main ones being *Diospyrus crassiflora* and *D. piscatoria*), and most of it, until shortly after the Second World War, came from isolated pockets of hill forest in southern Nigeria, Cameroon and Gabon, the Diospyrus genus as a whole, containing as it does several hundred species, was well represented among the forests of the West African coast. Quite a number of those species never attained much more than 'walking-stick' diameters, but a few did grow to sizes substantial enough to prove useful to the inhabitants of the forest, reaching bole diameters of 30 centimetres or more. Even at those comparatively large diameters the heartwood was rarely completely black but could be quite varied in colour, ranging from pure white to a most attractive greenish-black, with ochre, grey and chocolate streaks running through the black. The timber was always very hard indeed, regardless of colour, and resistant to termite attack. Because of this, it was very often used in pole form for house building. Spoons and combs were commonly made from it, too.

The fresh inner bark was used by 'bush doctors' as poultices for boils and arthritic swellings. Decoctions from the boiled leaves were often given as a treatment for sores.

The name used by many tribes for most species of Diospyrus was 'Elephant Skin', because the black roughness of the bark reminded them of the hide of the forest elephant. While the bark of young trees was quite thin, that of mature trees was thick, deeply fissured, steel-hard, and splintery. Sawmill operators soon found that it paid them to have the bark removed manually before sending ebony logs through their headrig saws. Failure to do so was likely to result in a set of shattered saw teeth and workers diving for cover as salvos of bark shot round the mill like shards of broken glass exploding from a cannon.

An additional and hitherto unsuspected unpleasantness, which I discovered while attempting to dry some blocks of ebony in one of the spare bedrooms of my house, was that at least one (alas, uniden-tified) species of ebony, while drying, emitted a penetrating and quite appalling 'tom-cat' smell which curtains, bedding, cushions and clothing absorbed like blotting paper, a stench that would lin-ger in the memory long after it had been eradicated from one's immediate surroundings. It was an aroma that was to transform my domestic life for a time. It not only brought about the resignation of two of my faithful house staff, but hastened the hurried departure, shortly after their arrival, of the British Ambassador and his lady never again to darken my doorstep.

Most timber manuals would have it that ebony timber dries rapidly and with little degrade. I confess here and now that I did not wait to find out in this case. The source of the smell having at last been identified, the billets were handed over to a Fanti fisherman with explicit instructions that he should take them in his canoe into the Gulf of Guinea and consign them deep down to the habitat of the hammerhead and the barracuda.

*   *   *   *   *

THE SEMI-DECIDUOUS FORESTS of Africa are most pleasant places to wander through, especially after one has endured a longish spell in the wet perpetual gloom of the evergreen forests. The air has an unfamiliar crispness to it and the harmattan mists that descend each night, in direct contrast to the steamy hotness of the rainforest, are cold enough at times to warrant the wearing of a jumper. The days are a melody of birdsong, and dead leaves crackle dryly underfoot as you walk beneath the trees. Colobus, green monkey and guenon chatter and bark and twitter in the high tops, while wild cat and golden cat prowl the ground below them. Animals are easier seen in such forests, too, for the undergrowth is more sparse and such vegetation as there is seems somehow less pervasive and smothering and threatening than in the humid southern forests.

Swamp – and, indeed, ground water of any kind – is kept at an acceptable minimum here, so one rarely encounters those horrendous tangles of vegetation that are the bane of one's life in the rainforests proper – incredible morasses of thorny raffia fronds, thorny vines, thorny grasses, thorny saplings, thorny EVERYTHING – and which often take hours, if not days, to cut a path through or find a way around.

There is a sense of tranquillity about those semi-deciduous forests so favoured by the entandrophragma clan, an aura of well-being that is never quite with one in the dense fecundity of the evergreen forests, where Fate seems to be waiting to grab you with hairy claws and sharp green teeth around every corner. In the evergreen forests, you can never afford yourself the luxury of feeling completely at ease with your surroundings. Danger, a voice keeps whispering in your ear, is all around you. This is nonsense of course, and you know it. But the voice persists, and when you find yourself all alone in the depths of such forests and hemmed in on all sides by a plethora of soggy green vegetal chaos, it is a voice that is difficult to ignore. Your eyes and ears are on red alert for the horrors that must be hiding before you and behind you and every nerve-end in your body seems to prickle with the fire of glowing needles, such is your state of watchfulness. While deep down inside you know that a mad bush cow is not waiting for you behind every clump of greenery and that not every fallen tree lying across your path has a cobra or a gaboon viper curled up behind it, still . . .

I rested in early morning sunshine on a steep slope at the foot of the craggy Nimba Range in northern Liberia. It was Sunday, the dry season was upon us, and the world was at peace. I was on my own in the forest, my back leaning against the buttress of a tree, and there was not even the faintest of zephyrs to stir the leaves around me. For all I knew or cared, I could have been the only human being left on earth, such was the stillness on that morning.

There was a heady perfume in the air and it was familiar. I lay back and looked upward through half-closed eyes, straight up along the glorious tubular perfection of the trunk of the tree to where, without any visible tapering, it suddenly branched out against the sky. The mighty crown was bereft of leaf at this time of the year and the filigree of its branches was etched in black silhouette against the empyreal blue of the heavens like some ancient Oriental scroll painting.

I looked around me. Near to where I sat a small mound of grey wood ash, already beginning to dissolve into the hard laterite soil, indicated the recent presence of a hunter. Or more likely, I thought, the most recent in a long succession of hunters. I wondered how many generations of hunters had sat where I sat now, century upon century of them, waiting under this forest giant for the little antelope that came in from the surrounding undergrowth to feed on its fallen fruit when the moon was high? How many of those hunters had mused, as I now did, about the tales this tree that sheltered them could tell if it could only talk? What strange creatures, I wondered, had rubbed their backs against its buttresses through countless dry seasons and rain seasons, and what disparate races, how great a diversity of individuals, had revelled in the sheer magnificence of this tree, while they idled the hours away as I did now in its sweetly feminine fragrance?

Sapele, sapelewood, aboudikro – all of those names have been given to it by the men of timber. *Entandrophragma cylindricum*, the men of science call it: '*Entandrophragma*', from the Greek '*en*' for 'in', '*andros*' for 'man', and '*phragma*' for 'partition', referring to the partitions between the staminal tube of the flower and its disc. Even the 'cylindrical' part of the scientific name refers not to the shape of the tree bole but to its fruits.

118

How convoluted! As always, the bush Africans did these things better. Local tribes called it 'Bower of the Gods', from their belief that their heavenly deities rested amidst the perfumed splendour of its massive branches when they had tired of travelling to and fro across the firmament.

As names went, it was no contest.

Chapter 11

Soft Woods in Sunlit Places

Botanical Name	–	*Ceiba pentandra*
Trade Name	–	Cottonwood
Other Names	–	Fromager (Ivory Coast) Okhar (Nigeria) Kapokier (Zaire)
Distribution	–	The tropics
Timber	–	White to light grey, with pinkish tinge and pale yellowish grey streaks. Cross-grained, coarse and light. Dries well. Easily worked, but very difficult to obtain good finish.
Commercial Uses	–	Sound insulation, core stock, crates and basic carpentry.

'*F*ROMAGER', THE FRENCH call it. Cheesewood. Whether it was a sobriquet originally applied because of the extreme softness of the wood or because one of the more common early uses of the timber was for making cheese boxes in France, is of no moment. While it could be said that it is an accurate description of the timber, it has always seemed to me to be rather an irreverent term for such a magnificent specimen of tree. For there is not doubt that *Ceiba pentandra*, the cottonwood, is one of the most attractive trees in all Africa when seen at its majestic best in a favourable setting.

It is a massive tree, often reaching a height of 60 metres or more and a diameter of 2 metres. At this height the tree will often be branchless to a height of 40 metres, the great, sprawling, heavily branched crown then taking up the top 20 metres. A curious but common feature of the crowns of such mature trees is the way in which the far-spreading main branches, jutting out at right angles from the trunk, send up vertical shoots from the arms of the branches like the teeth of a gargantuan comb.

When seen growing in a high forest situation the bole is usually beautifully cylindrical, but in open spaces it can sometimes assume a rather lumpy and bulbous character. The bark is shiny-smooth and a light ashy-blue-grey in colour. The buttresses can be variable in shape and size, mainly depending upon the conditions in which the tree happens to be growing. In high forest, buttresses can be of moderate size, while in secondary forest, farm clearings and in the proximity of towns and villages they are often massive and wide-spreading. The stems, and usually the branches as well, of young trees are heavily armed with thick sharp-pointed spines. These grad-ually disappear with age, but some, less sharp and much more scattered, remain on the buttresses throughout the tree's life.

The attractive leaves are compound, with the five to nine shiny dark-green leaflets spreading from the same point at the top of the leaf-stalk like the fingers of a hand. The tree becomes deciduous during the early days of the dry season in November and December. It is soon after this that the pale yellow tassel-like flowers appear on the bare crown. Just after dusk, bats come swarming around the tree in clouds at this time of the year, for the flowers open at night and their penetrating and highly unpleasant odour seems to be particularly attractive to these nocturnal creatures.

The fruits are long green capsules (about 30 centimetres long by 7 centimetres wide) packed with tiny black seeds which are embedded in soft white kapok. These capsules ripen during the latter part of the dry season, most of them opening on the trees to release the seeds with their attendant strands of kapok. Some fall to the ground unopened, to burst on impact.

This is the time of the year when one of the real spectacles of the rainforests is seen. Drive along a logging track in open forest and you are liable to find yourself suddenly in the middle of what would at first appear to be a blinding snowstorm, so dense that your wipers have difficulty in clearing your windscreen. This is kapok from the cottonwood seedpods, and the air is thick with it, some-times so thick that, when walking through it, breathing becomes impossible without a handkerchief over the mouth, so dense that the ground and the roadside vegetation soon becomes white with it. Under the parent tree, when you locate it, you will find that the earth is covered with a layer of kapok several inches deep.

Kapok is a remarkable substance. The word itself is an old Malay word for a tree that grows in abundance in Malaysia, as indeed it does on virtually every land mass in a broad belt some 10 degrees north and south of the equator right around the world. The kapok itself is as light as thistledown. It is a lustrous, silky fibre, composed mainly of cellulose. The fibres are filled with air and are non-absorbent, making the substance very buoyant, a characteristic that has made it useful in the past as a cork substitute in such items as life jackets. Curiously, it is also vermin proof, and there was a time when it was very much in vogue for the stuffing of mattresses and pillows. For the first half of the 20th century there was, therefore, quite a thriving export trade in kapok, although the bulk of it centred around Indonesia, where the industry was much more co-ordinated and professional. There was particular emphasis on this trade during the years of the two World Wars, when it was much in demand for the lining of pilots' flying jackets. Today, as with so many other things, this wonderful natural substance is being replaced with man-made synthetics, which are cheaper and easier to produce and tend to last longer.

The kapok was also put to good use in Africa, for stuffing cushions and pillows and so on. In the more open areas of fringing forest, where the plank buttresses could often be high and extensive, they would sometimes be sawn or hacked off the standing tree and used as slabs in village compounds for drying clothes or coffee-and-cocoa beans. The seeds were reputed to yield a stearine-rich oil, used at one time in the manufacture of soap and cattle-feed, but I confess that in all my time in Africa I never saw or heard of them being utilized for anything at all.

The tree was sometimes planted in the vicinity of villages and towns. Indeed, in otherwise deserted places within the forest, the presence of a solitary cottonwood tree would often be an indication of the site of a long-abandoned village, just as the site of a solitary rowan tree standing out on its own amidst a waste of bracken on the side of a Scottish mountain was usually an indicator of the site of some long-forgotten croft. Since African villagers rarely planted anything unless they were paid for it, or the plant was guaranteed to be of specific future use to them, why the cottonwood should have been held in such esteem was not always clear to the newcomer to the country, for it is not even of much use as a shade tree. The crown, though large and spreading, is not dense, and it is, in any case, bare of leaf during the hottest months of the year. In addition, the soft brittle nature of its timber make its huge branches a positive hazard to anyone below it during the high winds and the constant lightning strikes that herald each rain season.

The real reason for the tree's popularity is spiritual. Just as in Scotland the rowan tree was planted in remote places in the belief that it would help ward off evil spirits, so the cottonwood in Africa was regarded as being of great significance in a variety of juju practices. However, this only referred to trees growing in the vicinity of certain villages or at designated sites of worship and not, usually, to those growing wild within the high forest.

The timber is dull and unattractive. It is highly perishable, and after felling must be sprayed with fungicide and insecticide. As soon as the logs have reached their intended destination, they must be converted and dried without delay. Despite those drawbacks the timber has found a niche in the overseas markets for sound insulation, plywood core stock, crates and boxes, and rough carpentry. Material from young trees is best; large old trees are often rotten inside. The experienced logger will recognise this by the abnormal swelling of the bole. If not actually rotten, the tree will be afflicted by the condition known as brittle heart, which is often the precursor of terminal decay.

There are some scientists who believe that the cottonwood's original home was in South America, and that it was introduced to other tropical continents through seed attached to kapok drifting with favourable winds and sea currents, or even by early seafaring explorers. Yet others believe it to have originated in Africa. Whatever the truth of the matter, *Ceiba pentandra* has succeeded in making itself at home in more parts of the tropics than probably any other species.

A closely related species is known to the timber trade as the West African bombax, or *Bombax buonopozense*. In every aspect of its timber qualities, it is virtually identical. From a distance, the standing tree also looks the same, but closer examination shows it to have smaller and blunter buttresses, and indeed the general aspect of the tree is much less bulky than that of the cottonwood. It is also without the latter's characteristic prickles on the bole and buttresses, although it does have them on its branches. But when one sees it towards the end of the dry season, there can be little doubt as to its true identity, for its bare branches suddenly glow with scarlet. The thick-petalled waxy flowers are large – about 10 centimetres long and 5 centimetres broad – and in such profusion that when one is flying over the forest at dusk their dull red gleam jumps out from the darkness of their surroundings like incendiary flares. Duikers are avid eaters of the fallen flowers, and at this time of the year the trees are targeted by all forms of predators, both four-legged and two-legged.

Another species to be found in areas frequented by the bombax and the cottonwood is the alone, or *Rhodognaphalon brevicuspe*.

There are a number of similarities between the alone and the other two species, mainly in the fact that its timber is soft, not at all durable and is used for virtually the same purposes as the others. But its colour is quite different. The heartwood is a startlingly beautiful bright red when the tree is fresh-felled, but this rapidly turns to a not unattractive deep brownish red on exposure. The white-petalled flowers, about 4 centimetres in length, are full of long, rust-coloured stamens which, when the flower is open, make it look like the head of a paint brush. The fruit capsule is much smaller that that of the cottonwood but it has similar looking seeds, and these, too, are embedded in kapok, though kapok with a difference. The generic name for this species, *Rhodognaphalon*, is derived from the Greek for 'reddish-brown', and reddish-brown is a good description of the kapok. The pods open on the tree, at which time the kapok can be seen sitting en masse all over the top of the crown in thick piles of fluff, reminding one irresistibly of those ridiculous 'Jimmy Wigs' so beloved of Scottish soccer's 'Tartan Army' supporters on their pilgrimages around Europe during the latter part of the 20th century.

A large soft-timbered tree that always reaches for the sun rather than seek to merge with the anonymity of the perpetual shadows is the canarium or *Canarium schweinfurthii*. Canarium is a very handsome tree, common throughout the better-drained lands of the rainforests of the Coast. Indeed, its range stretches much further, for it may be encountered as far east as the highlands of Tanzania. Its timber has been known to the Europeans for a long time. Unwin reports that it was sold in the Liverpool market at 1/6d per cubic foot in 1906 as 'Gaboon Mahogany'. It must have come as a distinct surprise to the discriminating sawmillers of that era to learn that this species should be classified as a mahogany. Canarium timber is certainly pleasing to look at but it bears no resemblance to any species of mahogany, African or otherwise. When newly felled it is of a most delicate bisque hue, darkening gradually to a most attractive pale-buff with a satiny lustre and a delicate scent. When quarter-sawn, it often exhibits a rather subdued but decoratively striped figuring. There are drawbacks, however: the texture is

126

coarse and wooly and the tree has a tendency towards spiral grain. It is also light and soft and not at all durable, rapidly turning to a horrible greyish-blue with fungal stains, and subject to the attentions of boring insects soon after felling. There are, in addition, decided difficulties in sawing as the cells are full of silica. This, combined with the lack of durability, creates problems in trying to impregnate the timber with preservatives.

The standing tree, however, is a real beauty. It is tall and cylindrical and graceful, with scarcely more than a slight basal swelling at the point where the bole leaves the ground. Thick roots extend snake-like every which way over the surface of the ground far from the tree, and these are identifying characteristics of the mature tree when all else fails. The crown, though massive, is of a surprisingly open nature, mainly because the long and delicate leaves – in shape, rather like those of the European ash – are clustered in tufts at the ends of the branchlets. The fruit is a hard nut covered by a fleshy outer layer and it is edible, being much prized by animals and humans alike. (In some areas, it is planted around villages because of this.)

The scaly, tan-coloured bark exudes a thick greyish resin when slashed, and it has a very strong odour of turpentine. Hunters and farmers hack at the bark when passing, with the result that large solidified lumps of resin gather around the base of the tree, like chunks of curdled milk in appearance. The resin is collected for use as candles and torches by hunters. It burns fiercely, but emits a thick black and fragrant smoke. At one time carbon black was collected in receptacles from the smoke and used for tribal tattoos. Rather more bizzarely, light-skinned village maidens wishing to improve their marital potential used it as eye shadow.

There were many medical applications for the resin, not all of which would meet the approval of the British Medical Association. I lived for a few months on the fringe of a leper colony near Cape Palmas in Liberia where I was shown by one of the inmate's wives – who were allowed to live on site along with their husband sufferers – how fresh inner bark was ground to a pulp in a mortar along with shavings of the solidified resin. Hot water was the added and the mixture applied to the leprous ulcers. Neither the patient nor his wife were allowed to eat catfish during the period of treatment, and sexual intercourse was totally forbidden. She found the catfish restriction particularly irksome, for catfish were the only type of fish available in those interior lowland forests. The sexual intercourse taboo, she informed me, troubled her far less, for this was easily obtainable on her sporadic trips out to the market in Cape Palmas, and that was quite sufficient for her. It helped to pay the bills, she said, which was the only interest the act had ever held for her.

In his book *West African Forests and Forestry*, written in 1920, A.E. Unwin remarks upon how pleasant-tasting he found the resin of canarium to be. One can only conjecture upon the great man's motive for eating the stuff in the first place: with many African tribes the resin of this species is reputed to be a sure-fire cure for gonorrhoea.

Another light demander is the ilomba, or *Pycnanthus angolensis*. This is never a tall tree by rainforest standards, nor is it ever of immense girth. It can attain a height of 30 metres and a girth of about 1.20 metres, but not often. Usually, it is of much more modest size, and it is often to be found where the forest is of an open secondary nature. In such a location, it may be encountered in quite large numbers.

Ilomba is another of those trees that, once seen is never forgotten, with its slender, angular bole and long, thin, ungainly-looking branches all gathered together in distinctive whorls around the quaintly flattened top of the tree. Both twigs and foliage are covered in a sort of ochre felt in the early stages, but even more characteristic of this species is the fact that its long lance-shaped leaves are invariably riddled with round holes through the attentions of leaf-boring insects, and these are easily visible from the ground.

This species belongs to the nutmeg family (*Myristaca fragrans*) and its fruits resemble those of the nutmeg. They are edible, and green pigeons feast on them throughout the fruiting season.

The timber is greyish-white with a vague silvery sheen. It is light and very easily split down the length of the grain. This feature made it popular for converting into rough-hewn planks in the south-west of Cameroon, where it was referred to as 'carraboard' in the pidgin dialect. Whole huts were built from it, the shingled layers of planks being used on sides and roofs, a practice I only rarely recall having seen anywhere else in Africa. The timber is not at all durable. However, unlike that of canarium, the wood soaks in preservatives like blotting paper and thus has found a ready overseas market for such as plywood core stock and general indoor joinery.

One personal memory I have of living in huts made of carraboard in Cameroon is that they were the most pleasant of all huts in which to stay, for even in the heat of the midday sun they stayed remarkably cool.

An interesting species favouring the drier parts of the rainforest regions was the erimado (*Ricinodendron species*). Particularly common in my time in open areas of fringing forest or old abandoned farmland, it was a tree that grew very rapidly indeed and could attain very respectable dimensions, up to 30 metres high and a metre in diameter. Its crown was wide-spreading but very open, and its leaves were remarkably like those of the European horse chestnut.

Erimado is a species that boasts one of the lightest timbers in the whole world, weighing little more than 200 kg/m3, and it has been successfully used as a substitute for balsa. Because of its long thin-walled fibres, it has also been tried out in the paper pulp industry in mixture with the more traditional spruces. It is a timber that is very easy to handle and work, so it is used throughout tropical Africa in the making of all kinds of utensils and light furniture. However, although nails penetrate it as easily as they would penetrate butter, it does not hold nails or screws well. Quite often fathers would make toys for their children from it. I once saw a splendidly crafted little replica of a logging truck made from erimado being towed on the end of a piece of string by a little boy on the outskirts of one timber camp. One of the main uses to which the timber is put in southern Nigeria is in the making of coffins, presumably because of the combination of availability and easy working. One of the names for it there is the 'putta-putta tree' – putta-putta being pidgin for 'mud' – though whether this referred to the softness of the wood or its connection with coffins and therefore with the earth was never made clear to me.

A splendid little tree often found in those drier, more open parts of the rainforests is *Spathodea campanulata*, sometimes erroneously labelled the 'tulip tree' by European loggers. The true tulip tree, *Liriodendron tulipifera*, does not grow in Africa; it is a native of the eastern part of the United States and belongs to the magnolia family. I have seen both species, and I have to say that in appearance I find the African one to be just as spectacular as the one from the Allegheny Mountains.

Spathodea campanulata is not a large tree. It is rarely more than 15 metres tall and 0.50 metres in diameter. In the midst of the evergreen forests it would be smothered by the others and so one tends to find it more often in the northerly fringing forests. Most of my encounters with it have been in the vicinity of rock outcrops, such as I found in the Ondo Forest Reserves of Nigeria, and always in situations in which it seemed to stand out on its own, like one of today's self-styled super-models flaunting herself to her admiring public.

Outside the flowering and fruiting seasons it is not a particularly impressive tree. The bole tends to be rather fluted, but in other ways it is somewhat reminiscent of the London plane tree. Its crown is rather small, with short, sturdy branches, and its light-brown bark flakes off in large scales. It is the flowers and the fruit that make it special, particularly the flowers. In the latter part of the rains and the early part of the dry season they cover the crown with their tulip-like inflorescences, except that they are twice the size of the tulip flowers that we know; a beautiful shining scarlet with bright golden margins. They make a truly magnificent show.

The fruits emerge in January, and they are striking, too. They are stiff long pods, tapering at each end, about 20 centimetres long by 3 centimetres thick, and they stand upright above the foliage like sentinels of a phantom Lilliputian army. Eventually, they split open, releasing masses of tiny winged seeds to whirr into oblivion when the first zephyrs whisper across the treetops.

The timber is white, very soft and coarse. I have never known it to be used for anything.

One of the most extraordinary looking trees in all the tropics must be the baobab (*Adansonia digitata*). Strictly speaking, this is not really a rainforest species at all. I have seen it growing in the very heart of the accepted rainforest regions, but only in the vicinity of settlements where, at some time in the past, it must have been planted by someone. Its more natural habitat lies further to the north in the region known as the 'dry woodland savannah', where it may often be encountered singly or in very small clumps among the tall grasses.

The baobab could, with some justification, be labelled the clown of the tree world. Its shape is so gross as to make it look comical. The trunk is vast and squat and bulging, dissolving into nothing abruptly where the first of its thick, stubby branches juts out suddenly from this apex. The crown, too, is squat, with the branches and twigs appearing proportionately much thicker and blunter than those of other species. The gunmetal-grey fibrous bark is often stripped off by itinerant Hausa and Fulani cattlemen for the making of ropes, sleeping mats, sacks and rough clothing. This constant debarking results in the trunk becoming even more deformed, and it adds considerably to its already preposterous appearance. As it can attain a diameter of 15 metres when it is at its optimum height of 20 metres, this is a tree that is readily recognizable from afar.

Its flowering and fruiting habit is equally bizarre. The large solitary white flowers hang down on the ends of their 30-centimetre-long stalks. Like those of the cottonwood (to which family it belongs), they open up at night and smell of old socks, an odour that attracts great numbers of bats to the trees. In fact, bats appear to be the main pollinators. The resultant large greenish-brown melon-shaped fruits, with their rock-hard woody epidermic coverings, hang like Hallowe'en lanterns on the end of each stalk. This fruit is commonly known as 'Monkey Bread', and each one contains many small seeds buried in an acidic furfuraceous pulp.

When food is scarce, the pulp may be eaten by humans, but more often it is eaten by baboons who, as a result, appear to be almost entirely responsible for the distribution of this species across the woodland savannah region. They will carry the large capsules

131

considerable distances from the parent tree until they find a quiet spot in which to crack them open with their fearsome fangs. On one occasion I was driving a Land-Rover along the Kabba to Lokoja dirt road in northern Nigeria when I spotted a large male baboon perched on a concrete milestone at the side of the road, endeavouring to open one of those fruits. I kept a watchful eye on the creature as my vehicle approached it, for I have always been wary of baboons. Suddenly, as I drew level with where it was sitting, the ape, patently irritated at its lack of success in opening the friut, hurled it at me with all the venomous intent of a simian Freddy Trueman. The object ricochetted off the metal frame-work just behind my head with the force of an exploding shell. A later examination showed a very sizeable dent in the frame, and the ape was probably still laughing years later when he was telling his grandchildren about the fright he gave me.

Baobab timber is soft and light, and worthless for anything other than firewood. It is not even good for that unless it is dead and thoroughly dried out, for much of its 'timber' content is taken up with water-storage tissue. It is a tree that is reputed to live for over 1,000 years and, along with the cottonwood, is often regarded as sacred when growing in the vicinity of villages or towns. In the past it had a reputation for being associated with singularly unpleasant sacrificial rites. Indeed, legend had it among some tribes that the dark streaks often found running through the timber from very old trees was caused by blood from the many victims done to death at their foot in ages past.

*　　*　　*　　*　　*

JUJU IS AN integral part of African society, and in my day there were any number of small and otherwise insignificant trees which, for one reason or another, were worshipped by tribes. One very common shrub of forest clearings and open spaces, *Harungana madagascariensis*, was a most useful plant if it was your desire to visit ill-fortune upon your neighbour. It only required a visit to your local witchdoctor, the payment of the going rate for such services, and he would, by the judicious preparation of a potion from the foliage of this species, introduce to the object of your disaffection such unpleasantries as vertigo, boils, impetigo, mange, insanity and stoppage of urine. It would cost you a lot more to ensure your neighbour's departure to a far, far better world than this, but that, too, could be arranged via the same species for a correspondingly fatter fee.

Just to show that the nations of the 'civilized' world did not have the copyright on sharp practice, another common but relatively unknown species was much used by witchdoctors as a medium for one of their more outrageous scams. The various members of the Memecyclon family are understorey trees with small, deep-purple berries somewhat resembling the fruits of the European elderberry. The hedonist seeking an easy way to the achievement of good health, instant wealth, and a life in which the moral standards of the fair sex were at a satisfactory low level, had only to approach his friendly witchdoctor who would – again for an agreed fee – introduce his client to the particular tree in which dwelt the spirit that might accept him as a 'favoured one'. Following the introduction, the client had to bring a gift to lay at the foot of the tree. If, by the following morning, the gift had vanished, it could be assumed by the gratified client that it had been accepted by the spirit and that his future prosperity was assured.

Witchdoctors were as unscrupulous as politicians. They were also very rich people.

To the casual observer, however, the most obvious of the juju trees were those most easily seen. All tribal areas had their own special juju tree, almost always a huge and venerable tree visible from far away, either at the outskirts of a village or at the edge of the tribe's designated 'devil bush'. Loggers cast their greedy eyes upon such trees at their peril.

For a short period of time I was in charge of a large American logging company in Liberia. One of the the outstanding contracts on our books at the time I was appointed was for the felling and export of a parcel of 'fromager' – or cottonwood – to Holland. It proved to be a surprisingly difficult contract to fulfil for, although common enough in that area, the timber had to be shipped immediately after felling due to its extreme vulnerability.

There was one unanticipated headache suffered by me in the fulfilment of this contract. On the outskirts of the tribal headquarter town of Juarzon there stood a magnificent solitary cottonwood. Having been warned that this specimen was most sacred, I had issued strict instructions that in no circumstances should it be touched. The inevitable happened. A chainsaw operator with a grievance against the town chief, me, and life in general, flattened it. The dust had barely settled around the fallen giant when all hell broke out around me. Predictably, much of the hellfire was stoked up by 'Newspaper George'.

Newspaper George was a singularly ugly little Kruman. He was an albino and quite intelligent, but almost rabidly anti-white. He had been a thorn in my flesh ever since I had arrived in Liberia, for he was a reporter for the *Monrovian Daily Times*.

All Liberians dislike white colonials but, most of all, they are very much against British colonials. I had rapidly made myself *persona non grata* with the local dignitaries by putting an instant block on all the nice little backhanders which had previously been doled out to them to 'keep them sweet'. As one of the main recipients had been Newspaper George, his articles about me became more and more vitriolic. Now and again he would leave his office in Monrovia to travel up in the little coastal passenger plane to harrass me. Actually, I got on quite well with him in those face-to-face encounters, for he amused me in a perverse sort of way. In true West African fashion, his dislike of me as a colonial did not stop him from laying waste to my gin and my food when he came to my house.

He had a field day over the felling of the juju tree, and neither my abject letter of apology and substantial 'compensation' to the town chief – gratefully accepted by the latter – could stem George's torrent of invective. His subsequent article was libellous to the nth degree, so much so that, by his next visit, even he realised he had gone too far. He was unusually quiet as we walked to my house. I poured him his usual libation and we sat opposite one another, saying nothing by eyeing each other silently. On the little table between us lay the offending issue of his newspaper.

I picked up the paper and read out aloud: 'With typical white arrogance, this brutal English colonial seeks to destroy our national heritage by ordering his hired quislings to fell all our sacred trees . . .'

I laid the paper down and gazed coldly at him. He lifted his drink and smiled uncomfortably.

'Well?' I said.

'Well what?'

'What have you got to say for yourself?'

'I have a job to do!' he replied defensively.

There was a longish silence. He began to chuckle and I relaxed. George, I realised, was just winding me up again. I raised my glass. We touched glasses across the table and he said: 'Cheers!'

'I could have taken your comments with reasonable equanimity,' I remarked at last, 'Except . . .'

'Yes?'

'I happen to be Scottish,' I reminded him stiffly.

Newspaper George smirked. 'I figured *that* would hurt most of all!' he remarked smugly.

Chapter 12

The Missionary Tree

Botanical Names	–	*Milicia regia* and *M. excelsa*
Trade Name	–	Iroko
Other Names	–	Odum (Ghana) Kambala (Zaire) Moreira (Angola)
Distribution	–	Sierra Leone to Tanzania
Timber	–	Golden brown, with coarse, interlocked grain. Hard deposits of calcium carbonate ('stone') sometimes present. Takes good finish. Nails, screws and glues well.
Commercial Uses	–	Ship/boat building; flooring; sliced veneer; laboratory benches; furniture.

SINCE THE EARLY part of the 20th century there has been considerable controversy among the Great Men of Science as to what botanical name to append to the iroko tree. Throughout my life in Africa, it was known by the resounding name of *Chlorophora regia* or *Chlorophora excelsa*, depending mainly upon whether the tree happened to be growing in the wetter parts of the rainforest or in the drier semi-deciduous forests on the northern fringes of the rainforest zone. (*Chlorophora regia* was adjudged to belong to the former.) Now, the '*Chlorophora*' section of the two names has been replaced by the new name of '*Milicia*'.

Milicia regia, Milicia excelsa, let the eggheads call it what they will, the timber remains the same. Neither African nor European differentiate between the two. And if '*Milicia*' sounds far too effeminate for this upright Rock-Of-Ages-looking tree, at least the boffins had the good sense to leave the '*regia*' and '*excelsa*' bits as they were.

For this is a truly splendid and regal tree. Especially when you come across it in circumstances that show it to its best advantage, perhaps towering high above a sea of cassava in an otherwise treeless patch of farm, or all on its own on the outskirts of a village as you approach in your car.

Of all the better known timber trees to be found in Africa, the range of the iroko is probably the most far-reaching. In any area of wooded landscape between Freetown and Zanzibar – and sometimes even in relatively open expanses of fringing savannah – one is liable to meet up with it. It has an air of distinction about it, and once you have had the first one pointed out to you, it is unlikely that you will fail to recognize the next one you see.

It is a tall tree, growing to 45 metres or more in height and up to 2.5 metres in diameter. The stem is beautifully cylindrical and straight, though, on the very large trees, it occasionally adopts a peculiarly angular posture. It has no buttresses to speak of; none at all, in fact, in the younger trees, but in the older trees quite heavy root swellings will develop. The bark is thick and rough and very scaly, with numerous prominent yellow lenticels on the upper side of the surface roots. In high forest, the bark is black, but in the open it adopts a metallic grey hue.

A chip – or 'slash' – taken from the bark of a growing tree can often give important clues in tree identification. Iroko slash is as hard as stone and very granular. It is bright yellow to ochre in colour, with vividly white streaks through it, and it almost immediately begins to exude a creamy white sticky latex.

When growing in open conditions, the crown has a very characteristic deltoid shape, with branchlets and foliage clustered tightly together within that triangle. Seen from a distance against the sky, the dark bottle-green of the foliage combined with this dense packing gives the crown an appearance almost of blackness.

From January to March, at the height of the dry season, this funereal hue softens dramatically to a much lighter shade as masses of long yellow male catkins and shorter light green female catkins suddenly appear. By April, these will have turned into long flattened pulpy fruits containing numerous tiny nuts. These fruits are avidly eaten by just about everything that crawls, walks and flies in the African rainforest regions, which may help to explain both the unusually wide-ranging nature of this species and, conversely, the reason why one will never find iroko-dominant forest anywhere in Africa. While the fruit is eaten and spread by animals and birds in the normal way, the tiny nuts contained within are also attacked with relish by a galling insect.

Whatever arguments the scientists may have had about the naming of this species, it has long been agreed that iroko produces an excellent timber. Its value as a timber tree had, of course, always been known to the indigenous African but the fact that a particular timber had some value in its native land did not necessarily make it export material. It was a long haul from point of felling in Africa to the market places of Europe, and much degrade could take place in logs even between stump and shipping point in Africa, never mind the period while they were crammed in the hold of a ship on their slow journey northward through the Bay of Biscay. Durability – or its lack – was a key factor in determining the export potential of any timber. Nor did the fact that a tree looked grand while it was standing mean anything at all to the prospective exporter, particularly in those early days before the arrival of fungicides and insecticides. Three species, in their own unique ways, were perfect examples of the fact that, in the world of the timber man at least, good looks do not necessarily mean satisfaction even when one has succeeded in getting the object of one's desire in a horizontal position:

Probably the most magnificent of the three is the silk cotton tree (*Ceiba pentandra*). It is mighty of bole, perfectly cylindrical and totally free of branches for – often – 30 metres of its length. It grows everywhere on the Coast, and it was probably one of the first really large trees to be seen by the early Portuguese explorers when they anchored offshore anywhere along the Gulf of Guinea. It must have been a considerable disappointment to them to find that its timber is as soft as cardboard and everything in Africa attacks it from the moment it hits the ground after felling.

Eveuss (*Klainedoxa gabonensis*), has almost equally fine proportions, but in this case the timber is so hard that axe heads of the finest steel were quite commonly shattered when attempts were made to fell it. Indeed, even today this species has made no impact on the export market because of its hardness, sophisticated modern machinery being unable to do very much with it. It is one tree that farmers make no attempt to fell when clearing areas of forest for their rice and yam farms.

Lolagbola (*Oxystigma oxyphyllum*) is tall and has a bole as straight as a ruler. Large tracts of this lovely tree could, at one time, be found throughout the rainforest from Nigeria to Angola. The tree, however, was found to be so saturated with gum in both sapwood and heartwood that it clogged up saws and tools and made it quite useless for timber exporting.

Iroko, however, proved that not only did it look good, it *was* good. Its value was tested in 1906 when, predictably, a few sample logs were sold on the Liverpool market. The price quoted then was five pence per superficial foot. It was the best bargain since the United States of America bought Alaska from the Russians.

Today its timber is used throughout Europe and America for a wide range of purposes, from railway sleepers and wharf piling to decorative wall panelling. While it does not possess any of the figuring of the mahoganies, nevertheless it is an attractive timber of a golden brown shade, darkening with age to the colour and sheen of old brasswork. Slightly oily to the touch, it is a hard and tough timber, but surprisingly easy to work with all kinds of tools. It is most durable: the heartwood is almost totally resistant to all preservatives, but, as I know of no boring insect ever bred in Europe with powerful enough drilling equipment to make much impression on this timber, preservatives are not necessary in this case.

One defect occasionally found in the standing tree is lumps of 'stone', or, more correctly, a rock-hard deposits of calcium carbonate. These may appear at random in some trees, and in others, not at all. No one seems sure why this annoying defect should occur in some trees and not in others, and scientists seem unsure as to the reason for its presence at all. In my own experience, there were specific areas in which the incidence of 'stone' was quite high, while in others it was so low as to be either negligible or non-existent. These 'stone' deposits could be quite chunky in size – I have seen them as large as 40 centimetres in diameter, and as they were invariably buried inside the trunk, with no obvious sign of their presence until the saw hit them, they could be an awful nuisance to any sawmiller unlucky enough to receive a parcel of logs from a badly affected area.

The iroko was one of the most valued of all trees to the African. Kings and chiefs who considered themselves to be a bit above the common herd got their carpenters to make ornate doors for their palaces and houses from its timbers, and they had fancy stools, washbasins, wall plates, food bowls and trinket boxes carved from it. Witchdoctors had their ceremonial masks made from it, and their juju huts were often completely furnished with the wood of the iroko. Missionaries of all denominations, never slow to take over such pagan rituals and ideas as suited their own ends, began to furnish their missions with it, and there are plenty of eminent churches and convents throughout West Africa today whose timbers, from flooring to rafters, originated from this most traditional of pagan symbols.

The original natives of the forest called the iroko 'The Juju Tree'. With true African irony, later generations were to refer to it as 'The Missionary Tree'.

Carving was an art at which many village carpenters excelled. An innovative Catholic missionary known to me made use of this expertise by having panels for church doors carved from iroko by one of his converts. He allowed the carver a fair amount of poetic license in his attempts to place on ligniform record the African's interpretation of Biblical events. As a result, somewhat bemused visitors to churches throughout the land began to find themselves confronted by church doors adorned with exquisitely engraved panels of black Marys pounding yams in mortars for the Last Supper and Fulani Wise Men bearing calabashes of palm wine on their heads to celebrate the birth of distinctly negroid Jesuses.

The tree itself remained a sort of shrine to a variety of juju beliefs. Its white latex was often taken in one form or another to promote fertility and lactation in women, and women would place plantains and yams at the foot of any iroko tree chosen as their juju tree so that they would be blessed with male children. Chiefs would sacrifice goats at it to propitiate malevolent witches who were supposed to hold court within it when the moon was at its zenith. There was one area in which I worked briefly where a chief whose wife had failed to conceive within the stipulated six months trial period was expected to take both wife and sleeping mat to the foot of the juju iroko and remain there until the job was done. It was a practice that had never been known to fail, though there were rumours that the late incumbent to the title had had to resort to a certain amount of knavery to maintain the reputation of the tradition. He had been in his dotage and was very frail when he had rather ambitiously purchased a very young and superbly active wife. Finding that, even with the influence of the iroko tree lowering over them, he was unable to raise the necessary head of steam, he had approached the witchdoctor. As it was not in the latter's interests to have the locals believe that the powers of his juju tree were waning, and it was definitely not in the old chief's interests to have them know that *his* powers were, alas, a thing of the past, an alliance was forged. The witchdoctor was young and fit and more than willing to co-operate, as any red-blooded young fellow in his position ought to have been. In the fullness of time, a son was born, and two major crises had been skilfully averted.

When hidden in the gloom of a rainforest environment, the splendour of the iroko tree tends to be somewhat muted. The wet black coat of camouflage adopted by its bark in those conditions helps it to achieve this degree of anonymity. It simply becomes absorbed by its surroundings, and even when the eye suddenly lights upon its immense frame jutting up from a tangle of undergrowth, it never really stands out as one might expect, for it is but one of many large and almost equally imposing species in the vicinity.

It was in the Ekiti and Kabba regions of Nigeria that I probably saw iroko at its best. These areas were on the northernmost perimeter of the rainforest zone, and they were of quite stunning beauty, with rock formations of an almost Martian starkness jutting upward with startling suddenness out of the surrounding seas of long grasses and peasant farming. Kabba was on the southern fringe of what was known as the orchard savannah zone, where scrubby little bushes of apple-tree size predominated, with the occasional tall baobab or bombax or iroko tree standing like sentinels among them. Strips of evergreen forest clustered around the watercourses, and these were my reason for being so far to the north of my normal haunts.

The ancient cattle and market town of Kabba was situated some 80 kilometres by dirt road from Lokoja on the Niger. I was billeted in a government rest house situated on top of a tall hill on the outskirts of Kabba. The rest house was little more than a cement-faced, mud-walled hut with a roof of palm thatch, but it afforded a splendid panorama of the surrounding countryside, a luxury seldom to be encountered in my rainforests to the south. Also never to be seen in the humidity of the rainforests were the annual fires that swept the savannahs during December and January when the dry season was at its height and the grasses were at their longest and driest.

The fires were an impressive sight when seen at night from the vantage point of my rest house hill. I would watch the distant wall of flame, fifteen kilometres and more in length, sweeping inexorably forward in the blackness of the night, occasionally exploding upward like a solar flare in a spectacular display of pyrotechnics as the flames encountered some particularly flammable object. I would try to imagine the panic of all the wild creatures caught in their path, the more nimble footed fleeing before them and the slower ones being slowly but surely engulfed. By day, squadrons of vultures would soar and swoop over this bonanza of barbecued flesh left on the charred and still-smoking ground after the fire had passed on its way. A month after I left the area for good, the rest house itself was burned to the ground as the fires swept over the hill on which it stood.

The old colonial regime was on its way out in those days and the white administrators were gradually being replaced by Africans. The District Officer in charge at Kabba was a pleasant young Hausa. We were having a drink together on my rest house verandah one evening, listening to the sounds of Africa all around us, when from somewhere out over the darkened plains came a faint but eerie call, a long drawn out, chilling, cackling, bubbling cry that momentarily stilled all the other sounds. I though that I was familiar with most of the night sounds of West Africa, but this was a new one to me. 'What in hell was that?' I asked my young friend. 'Hyaena,' he replied succinctly.

It should not have surprised me, for this part of the world reminded me of the pictures I had seen of the great plains of East Africa. In fact, a subsequent browse through the records and diaries left by administrators earlier in the century – a facility kindly allowed me by the District Officer – showed that in the not too distant past creatures unknown in the more southerly rainforests but familiar to every East African veteran had roamed those savannahs around Kabba, perhaps never in great abundance but certainly in sufficient quantity as to be encountered from time to time by administrators when on tour of their areas. One – who sounded as though he would have been a cartoonist's delight – recorded in his diary: '. . . I was being transported on my litter round a bend in the Choka-Choka (a range of rocky hills between Kabba and Lokoja) when we encountered a lioness lying with her two cubs by the side of the track. My porters were all for dropping me and running for their lives, but I insisted that the bounders should carry me past the animal in a civilized and British manner.'

He probably didn't spill a drop of whatever he was drinking at the time.

No lions were left by the time I got there, though plenty of other wildlife remained. Coveys of partridge flew over the compounds of the government quarters, and huge flocks of guinea fowl settled on the road at the foot of the rest house hill in the early mornings, squatting in their dustbaths like domestic fowl. They made easy targets for my shotgun and were excellent to eat. Their idea of evasive tactics was to fly to the nearest tree and crane their long foolish necks at their pursuer.

The pockets of high forest around the watercourses in this savannah country were rarely more than twenty square kilometres in extent and more often only a fraction of that. In most of them the dominant trees were obeche (*Triplochiton scleroxylon*) and fig trees (*Ficus species*). Most of the dominant timber species, while just as impressive of girth as their rainforest siblings, tended to be a good deal shorter of bole, thus making them appear rather squat by comparison. This also applied to any iroko I saw, both in fringing savannah conditions and in the high forest itself.

There seemed, in fact, to be a greater proportion of iroko in this area than in any other part I had yet been to. What I had never come across before was the way in which soliatry specimens stood alone in the midst of all this scrub. Several were visible from my rest house. But even in the patches of evergreen forest, iroko trees were much more visible here than they tended to be in the rainforests. Perhaps this was because the open nature of those northern forests gave the sun better access, allowing it to reflect the silvery grey sparkle of the bark even in the heart of the forest.

One large forest tree I found in close association with the iroko in these parts, but in much greater numbers, was the ako (*Antiaris toxicaria*). The ako is of the same family as the iroko (*Moraceae*), and, externally at least, there are some similarities. It can reach similar heights and bole diameters as the iroko, and it is straight and cylindrical with a thick granular bark which exudes a watery latex when slashed. The leaves are quite similar in shape and their densely packed character can often give the crown the appearance of iroko from a distance. Its timber, however, bears no resemblance.

Ako timber is greyish yellow through and through, and it is both very soft and coarse in texture. Until the advent of modern preservatives the tree, handsome though it appeared on the surface, was generally avoided by the timber exporters. Even with rapid treatment, it had to be moved quickly from stump to processing point as it gets eaten by every insect under the sun and swiftly turns a horrible blue-mould shade through fungal agencies. Nevertheless its excellent preservative absorption qualities have made it a useful substitute in recent times for other, more highly prized white woods in utility plywood and interior joinery where lightness in weight is required and strength is not a necessary factor.

The forest African put the ako tree to use for many of the same things as the iroko. Ako was a favourite juju tree and its latex was of medicinal value to them, often for ailments known delicately as 'woman palavers'. The fibrous inner bark was stripped off, beaten with sticks and stones to make it pliable, and thoroughly washed to leach out the granular particles. The strips were then sewn together to make very serviceable sacks and even bush clothing. The timber was made into machete handles, stools and benches. The wood had the virtue of being extremely easy to carve, and the ordinary bushman cared very little about what the timber of any tree looked like so long as it served his immediate purpose.

Ako was a copious fruit bearer, and during the early part of each year it produced masses of little scarlet drupes about the size of cherries. The pulp surrounding the seed, like that of the iroko, was much sought after by birds and animals, and hunters would often take advantage of this to lie in wait around either tree to shoot whatever might come in sight. Duiker antelopes were particularly fond of ako fruit, and at dusk and in the early morning they would emerge from the forest to feed upon the fallen fruit, so making themselves an easy target.

On the fringe of a small area of forest not far to the north of the town of Kabba I came across two large ako trees and one iroko growing together. The branches of all three were heavily laden with fruit. The ground under the trees was carpeted a mottled red and brown with the fruit of the two species, and the damp soil was everywhere pitted with the tiny, sharp-pointed hoofmarks of duikers. A stream trickled its way slowly past the edge of the forest, and in a small hollow beyond the trees it had formed a sizable pool. The old hunter who was with me showed me some large hoofprints in the deep mud by the water and he told me that he had been hiding in some undergrowth behind the pool the previous evening when the animal that had made them had come to drink. 'I never see its like before in my life,' he shuddered, 'and I hope I never see it again.' He described it as being 'a mighty huge animal, with face like devil-horse and long bend-bend horns'. A hartebeest far from its normal range, I guessed. 'Why didn't you shoot it?' I asked curiously, for the average bush hunter would have shot his own grandmother had nothing else been available.

'Because,' he admitted frankly, 'I fear too much. De t'ing gave me evil eye and make horrible noise, so I bugger off quick.'

I waited by the pool over the course of two evenings and two mornings but I saw no sign of my old friend's *bête noir*. I did, however, see plenty of green pigeons and hornbills coming into the branches for a last snack before settling down for the night, and once a colony of vervet monkeys came briefly to plunder, only to be routed by a large vulture that plopped into the iroko top to glare balefully at them. On each of my evening vigils a pair of pretty little red-flanked duikers emerged timidly from the shadows of the forest to pick daintily at the fallen fruit, their russet coats glowing almost carmine with the redness of the setting sun, and just after dawn on the second morning a bushbuck appeared out of the mists to feed greedily, the white stripes on his chestnut-brown coat standing out with almost fluorescent luminance in the early light.

Before we parted, the old hunter took me to a strange rock formation which I had observed far off in the savannah, a jumble of colossal boulders that looked as though they had been set one on top of the other by some giant hand, the topmost one seemingly balanced so finely that it looked as though the most gentle of touches would send it rolling and crashing to the savannah far below. Behind the outcrop and hidden from my view until now were two ancient baobabs and two shattered iroko stumps, obviously the victims of a recent lightning strike. Between the stumps there was a large hole in the ground, obviously much in use. It stank, and clouds of blueflies buzzed lethargically around the entrance. 'Hyaena,' the hunter informed me. That night, as I sat alone with my whisky on the rest house hill, that long juddering cackle rang out eerily over the darkened plains, faintly in the distance but no less spooky-sounding for all that. I would not have been at all surprised to have learned that tonight was the Night of the Werewolf under those star-spangled African skies.

* * * * *

EIGHT MONTHS LATER I was leaving the area for good. It was mid-morning and heavy mists were slowly clearing. The road was in poor condition after the rains and my Land-Rover was reduced to a twenty-five kilometre per hour crawl as it clattered over the potholes and corrugations. Suddenly, out of the scrub savannah bordering the road emerged a large dog-like creature I had never seen before. It began to lope alongside my vehicle, just by my door and below my range of vision. At the same time I saw another come out of the bush on the passenger side. Spotted hyaenas. Two fully grown adults. I looked out of my little side window, down on to the back of the one loping beside me. It was maintaining exactly the same pace as the vehicle, a steady, easy lope, going no faster and no slower, just keeping pace with me . . . I noted the massive head, the sloping back, the broad muscular shoulders powering the front legs onward as it ran silently and relentlessly beside me.

I glanced at the wing mirror on the passenger side. Its mate was doing precisely the same. Synchronized pacing, a hyaena on each side of me.

I increased my speed as much as the road conditions would permit. My grisly pacemakers lengthened their stride comfortably to keep pace with me. Several kilometres down the road they were still loping steadfastly, silently, creepily, alongside the vehicle. Then, as though by some miracle of instant telepathy, they veered off into the elephant grass on their respective sides of the road and vanished. Suddenly, I was left with nothing but the endless empty track ahead of me and the wilderness of encroaching savannah all around me.

What had they been after? I wondered. Why had they followed me for so long and for so far? Vehicles were not common on that particular road in those days: did they think I was some new type of prey?

It was not until I reached the bitumen road some forty kilometres further on that I deemed it safe to stop and stretch my legs. I was sweating a little, still thinking about my strange encounter, still wondering. Perhaps, as someone was to suggest to me later, it had just been a game to them. Perhaps, in fact, they had simply been escorting me off their territory.

Perhaps. But it would have taken a more foolhardy person than I to have got out of that Land-Rover to test the theory back there on the Kabba road while those sinister undertakers were loping along so silently and with such purposeful determination by my side.

Chapter 13

The Farmer's Mahogany

Botanical Name	–	*Entandrophragma angolense*
Trade Name	–	Tiama
Other Names	–	Edinam (Ghana) Gedunohor (Nigeria) Timbi (Cameroon)
Distribution	–	Liberia to Angola
Timber	–	Reddish-brown, with rather coarse, interlocked grain and broad, irregular stripes on quarter-sawn surfaces. Easy to work with both machine and hand tools. Lustrous, and takes a high polish.
Commercial Uses	–	Decorative and plain veneer; furniture and office fittings; boat building.

As you lumber on your way above the shorline of the Gulf of Guinea in one of the Coast's ubiquitous Dakota passenger planes, you may spot the occasional tree, its bark silvery grey and sandpapered smooth by hot sea winds, towering upward like a lighthouse from the profligacy of mangroves and coconut palms and cassava patches down below. While the tree you are looking at is likely, more often than not, to be the omnipresent cottonwood, occasionally – just occasionally – you could be looking at a nomadic tiama, perfectly at ease in surroundings far removed from the normal haunts of others of its kind.

Of West Africa's four *Entandrophragmas* – tiama, sapelewood, sipo and kosipo – tiama is the most catholic in its choice of habitat. Like the others, it grows best and in greatest abundance in the drier, more northerly parts of the rainforest belt. Unlike the others, however, it may be encountered on any patch of reasonably well-drained terrain so far to the south throughout the evergreen forests as to come even within reach of the ocean.

This is one of West Africa's 'mahoganies'. As with the others of its genus, it is an arresting sight in maturity. It is an emergent tree: it likes the protection of shade in its formative years, but it prefers to have its crown basking in sunshine when it gets older. It can top 50 metres, and, at this height, it may reach a diameter of more than 2 metres. The bole is straight and cylindrical, completely devoid of branches for anything up to 30 metres, and its bark is variable in colour, from creamy-white in the full sunlight of open clearings to a most attractive reddish brown interspersed with large oyster-shell markings where plates of dead bark have fallen off the stem.

The crown is dome-shaped and densely green, except at the end of the rains, when it becomes – for a very short time – deciduous. In February its crown may also be transformed briefly to a bottle-green-and-dull-orange blanket by the masses of tiny flowers that suddenly appear on long stalks at the ends of the branchlets. The resultant fruits, cone-like and about 20 centimetres long, hang from the branchlets, ripening slowly throughout the remainder of the dry season and the first few months of the rains. Eventually a cargo of brown-winged seeds are released, looking like giant versions of those to be seen hanging in bunches from the European ash in autumn.

If the bole is a thing of beauty, the buttresses of an old tiama are truly spectacular, particularly where the tree is found growing on rocky terrain. In such conditions they can often extend far up the trunk, even as high as 6 metres, and they can spread in thick, sinuous walls about 2 metres high for more than 20 metres beyond the base of the tree, like the tentacles of some colossal squid. This, perhaps more than any other feature, helps distinguish it from the other mahoganies. I have, on occasion, sheltered for the night within those buttresses when caught by darkness far from my camp, but as scorpions, cobras and vipers also make occasional use of them, it is always wise to check out one's prospective lodgings carefully before venturing inside to settle down for the night.

Tiama will not grow in waterlogged areas. But should one of its seed, whirling on its single rotor-blade wing high over the forest in the warm winds, choose to land on some relatively dry oasis of land within a swamp, it will quite happily put its roots down right there. Like a *nouveau riche* building himself a mansion in the middle of a slum, the tiama will not only survive but will prosper mightily, oblivious to all the surrounding squalor.

Yet it is certainly in the drier parts of the rainforests that the tiama really flourishes. From Liberia and Angola in the west to Uganda in the far, far distant east, one is likely to come across it anywhere within the semi-evergreen forest regions of Africa.

Tiama has been well-known to dendrologists under a variety of botanical names since the middle of the 19th century. However, it was not to be until well after the Second World War that it was to find favour with the log exporters. Its timber was always regarded as being inferior in looks to that of its famous close cousin, the sapelewood, and only when stocks of the latter began to decline drastically did tiama finally gain recognition as a fully fledged member – albeit a junior one – of the Coast's great mahogany family.

There was no doubt, though, that in a market used to only the very best in mahoganies the exporter was slumming it somewhat when he found himself forced by circumstances to accept tiama in that very exclusive category. Scientific tests carried out on tiama proved generally unfavourable by comparison with sipo and sapele. Tiama was a timber that had to be dried with the greatest of care for it had a tendency to distort badly. It was found to be only moderately durable, and a major drawback was that it proved extremely resistant to preservatives. Logs stacked in forest landings needed constant attention owing to their vulnerability to the predations of powder-post beetles.

Nor did it compare at all favourably with the others in its working qualities. Although it responded quite well to hand and machine tools, the coarsely interlocked grain made planing difficult. It also tended to char badly during mortise work.

At first, its mechanical properties did not impress either. Most timber manuals listed it as possessing low bending strength and poor resistance to shock loads. A poor steam-bending classification, very low stiffness properties and only medium strength tended to send out an unpromising picture from the laboratories, and when all these early tests indicated that the species was not all that good for sliced veneering, the future did not look bright for tiama from the point of view of the timber exporter.

However, circumstances change. Necessity, as the old cliché would have it, is the mother of invention. As supplies of sipo and sapele began to dwindle, the favourable properties of tiama were suddenly given the emphasis they deserved. Tiama glues, nails and screws well, and – provided the grain is properly filled – it takes a good polish. Today, with factory machinery becoming ever more sophisticated, it has been found that even the occasional decorative veneer can be produced from it, and so it has been accepted as a good – if rather undistinguished – plywood species. At the same time, bad reputations, once acquired, are not easily overcome in the prejudiced world of timber, and it is likely that tiama will remain the poor relation of the *Entandrophragmas* for some time to come.

The forest African had no such snobbery about him. He liked the tiama tree, and it seemed to like him. Wherever I happened to stumble upon a clearing full of bananas or yams or rice or whatever on my travels through the forests, almost inevitably I would see a tiama growing somewhere in the vicinity. For this, truly, was the farmer's mahogany. When newly felled the timber was wet and sappy and relatively easy to convert into planks. Just as important, the planks would take nails without the slightest difficulty. The timber had that rich warm glow to it that all good mahoganies have, and it was, if anything, even more lustrous than some of its more famous cousins. It was true, of course, that it rarely had the beautiful figuring so often associated with the likes of sapelewood, but that mattered nought to the peasant farmer. His requirements from the timber were strictly utilitarian. He needed it for the making of tables, chairs, bed-frames, door planking and, occasionally, dugout canoes. It was very much an all-purpose timber to the bush carpenter and he would often be commissioned to make masks, food bowls and other household utensils from it, even though the coarseness of its grain was such as to make it difficult to smoothen even with the sharpest of metal scrapers.

Many different species could be found in association with tiama, for tiama is widespread in the rainforests. Two species with which I often found it growing were both, curiously enough, given the sobriquet of 'walnut' by long-forgotten European adventurers, one because its timber appeared to the layman similar to that of the European walnut, and the other because its fruit reminded them of the fruit of the latter species. Neither, however, have any connection with the true walnuts of Europe, Asia and America. Having discussed in Chapter 8 *Lovoa trichilioides*, a large forest tree whose timber is variously marketed under the names 'African walnut' and 'dibetou', I will confine my remarks here to the second 'walnut' variety, *Coula edulis*, which may be found anywhere in the rainforests from Sierra Leone to the Congo.

Here is one of Africa's more common trees, yet it is doubtful if even one timber exporter in a hundred will have heard of it. The dull, reddish-brown timber is extremely hard and durable, and it is completely resistant to attack by even the most persistent and voracious of boring insects. For this reason, poles of the species are occasionally used as doorposts and for roofing purposes by the village people, and as cross-pieces on log rafts by timber contractors. But it is strictly a tree of the forest understorey, and it never grows to a height or a diameter that would make it of the slightest interest to commercial loggers.

To all the denizens of the forest, however, the tree is of uncalculable value. Life in the rainforests would not be impossible for them without it, but its rich annual harvest does provide a guarantee that the vegetarians among them won't starve.

The fruit of the coula is a nut which does bear more than a passing resemblance to the fruit of the Eurasian walnut from the outside, both in shape and in size. The shell may be a bit harder to crack open but the result is well worth the effort. The kernel inside is meaty and good, unlike the wizened little walnuts that I all too often remember being my reward for the broken fingernails and bruised thumbs obtained in trying to extract them from their shells in my youth after raiding the old tree in the dentist's garden in Scotland.

The fruiting season lasts from the middle of November to the end of February, and each tree bears a copious quantity. The nuts have a very high fat content and are supremely edible, either in raw or roasted form. For many centuries they have been traded in countries far beyond the bounds of the rainforests.

There is another rainforest resident that likes the fruit of the coula tree, just as much as the humans do. Recent media publicity tends to suggest that the discovery that chimpanzees could use sticks and stones as tools is of very recent origin: in other words, since they were first seen doing so by intrepid white televison naturalists. This is about on a par with the claim that Christopher Columbus discovered America, conveniently forgetting the original natives whose home it was that Mr Columbus was in the process of discovering. Chimpanzees have been using sticks and stones to break open coula nut shells, I suspect, from the beginning of their time on earth, and will continue to do so for as long as coula nuts and chimpanzees get together. The fact that they have always been able to do so was well known to every black hunter that I ever encountered during my long career in the rainforests. It is many years since I first saw them at it, and I have to confess that it never occurred to me I was witnessing anything particularly remarkable. Indeed, it would have seemed odd to me if such highly intelligent creatures as chimpanzees had not been able to work out for themselves an easier and less time-consuming way of getting at what was inside the shells than by grinding at them with their teeth.

Coula-nut time in the rainforest is the nicest time of the year. The cool harmattan mists descend upon the forest canopy at night, to be replaced by around nine o'clock each morning with unremitting sunshine. It may be hot in the forest clearings, but it is cool where the coula trees are to be found midst the towering shadows of the forest giants around them. The trees hang heavy with bottle-green coula nuts at this time, ovoid drupes that ripen slowly to a dull reddish colour in the shifting glimmers of sunlight that manage to penetrate the overhead canopy. They drop as soon as they are ripe, and there is always a plentiful supply of them on the ground.

It is in these little glades around the coula trees that the chimpanzees gather. They sit crouched over their individual chopping blocks, looking for all the world like hairy garden gnomes, totally absorbed in what they are doing. The nut is held down firmly on the block between finger and thumb, then the nut-cracking tool of their choice – a stone or chunk of hard wood – is raised . . . CLACK . . . CLACK . . . CLACK then CRUNCH! The morsel is picked carefully from the shattered remains of the shell and transferred to the mouth, where it is rolled around the tongue with all the ostentatious relish of a *bon vivant* savouring a particularly fine wine. The hand reaches out again, and CLACK . . . CLACK . . . CLACK . . . the whole business starts all over again.

Chimpanzees in the wild have many a human characteristic. They are creatures of much humour, always game for a laugh when it is at the expense of others, with the adults joining in the youngsters' frolics when they have nothing better to do – though not when there is a coula-nut party on. Coula-nut business is deadly serious business and the playful interrupt it at their peril. But controlling bored and frisky youngsters is easier contemplated than managed, as parents of human children know only too well. I watched on one occasion as a very young chimp crept up behind an old lady of the troupe as she was attempting to pound a particularly recalcritant nut into submission. The rock in her fist was in mid-air and descending at speed towards the nut when the youngster barked suddenly and explosively to her immediate rear. Startled, she looked round. The stone hit her thumb and she bounded upward with a roar of rage while her erstwhile tormenter raced nimbly and gleefully up an adjacent tree.

On yet another occasion I watched as a young chimpanzee, stomach full to capacity, picked up a large green nut which had been left unopened. His eyes darted this way and that, looking for a target. The troupe leader, busy on his own at the edge of the glade, caught his attention. The nut, travelling with the speed of a meteor, zinged off the patriarch's skull. The old chap whirled round, a look of astonished outrage on his grizzled features, in time to see his assailant heading for the sanctuary of the surrounding undergrowth. Without hesitation, he hurled the rock which, moments before, had been his nut-cracker. The missile, weighing around a kilogram, sped across the clearing and missed decapitating the prankster by a whisker.

Even such minor contretemps were a rarity among the peaceful shadows of the coula trees. Mostly, the listener would hear nothing but the steady whacking of chimpanzees pounding methodically at the hard shells, while the mellow hooting of the little green pigeons in the surrounding mahoganies provided soothing orchestral accompaniment to a pasticcio of such tranquility as the fortunate observer was unlikely ever to experience in his life again.

I am well aware, of course, that tiama will be found in association with other tree species and other creatures. But this is a book of personal memories, and I write about those great forests as I choose to remember them. Tiama . . . coula nuts . . . chimpanzees . . . Whenever I think about one, I automatically think about the other two. The three are inextricably interwoven in my dreams of Africa.

There is one other creature of which I have very vivid memories while living in tiama-dominant forest. It is a creature that may, to the casual observer, possess little of the winsome attraction of the chimpanzee, but it, too, is a creature of high intelligence and it is equally family-minded. Scientists, for their own lofty reasons, have saddled it with the resounding, almost Wagnerian name of *Hylochoerus meinertzhageni.* To we lesser mortals, it is known as the 'Giant Forest Hog',

My first encounters with this colossal pig were in the Ivory Coast. I had been hired to mark out a road trace linking the N'zo and the Cavalla rivers, about twenty-five kilometres of which would run through tiama dominated mahogany forest. It was one of the most pleasant tasks I have ever been asked to do in my life. For much of the way the ground was undulating, but only gently so, and the incidence of really bad swamps was small. Where there were villages on the way I occasionally slept in them, and if there were none, I camped under the trees.

I preferred the latter, expecially at this time of the year when the dry season was upon us and the nights were at their coolest, thus maintaining the mosquito population at an acceptable minimum. Another reason for preferring to stay well away from villages was that in this area the sinister Snake Society was all-powerful, and during the harmattan time its members were at their most active. It was not that I had any reason to be afraid of their activities myself, but there were almost nightly mysterious rituals being performed in the village compounds that neither their women nor I were permitted to witness, and to have to remain locked up in a sweaty little room in a mud hut from dusk until dawn while these were in progress was not much to my liking.

However, so hospitable were the village chiefs and elders that it was often difficult to refuse their invitations to stay with them without causing offence. One of those villages, a tiny place of about a dozen huts called Tobliville, was clean and picturesque. It was situated on a little knoll surrounded by great boulders, among which grew giant tiama trees, their massive root flanges snaking every which way among the rocks.

On my first day there I was intrigued to find piled around the juju pole in the centre of the village an enormous heap of sun-bleached skulls, which looked at first sight as though they must have belonged to creatures unknown to modern man. Long and fearsome tusks, one on each side, jutted upward form the lower jaw. 'Na senior bush pig,' replied an old man laconically when I asked him what they were.

It was my first meeting with the animal known to us today as the giant forest hog. It was not to be my last; the very next day I encountered my first live ones.

An unseasonal storm had burst over the forest and I was hurrying through the downpour to the village. I rounded a corner of the track and found myself in the midst of them before they realised I was there. They exploded through the undergrowth from all around me with much grunting and snorting and squealing. They were gone in seconds, running like greyhounds, and I was left with nothing but a vision of huge, black, hairy shapes scattering to all points of the compass in the hissing rain.

Later that night a village hunter shot a large male and I was able to examine the body in the morning.

It was colossal. (I have since read that this species is the largest of the wild pigs.) Around 200 centimetres long, it must have stood about 100 centimetres high and weighed perhaps 250 kilograms. It was all muscle, with little of the obvious fat of the domestic pig. It had most curious looking, very large and hard projections on each cheek, found only in the adult male, I was informed. These were used as shields in the constant battles for supremacy with other males. The creature was covered in long, black, wiry hair and it stank like hell.

Its tusks, though, were what really caught my eye. They were enormous: I measured each – 29 centimetres long – but was informed by the hunter who shot the hog that this particular pair of tusks was not unusually large. The record trophies were always kept in the huts of the chief and the witchdoctor; lesser ones, such as this pair, would join the others around the juju pole in the village compound.

There were many tales of hunters being attacked by large male hogs, and I have no doubt that some of the stories were true. No animal grows tusks like that purely for decoration. But, although I was to come upon them almost daily during my time in that area, none ever showed the slightest aggressive intent towards me.

* * * * *

I HAVE MANY memories of 'The Farmers Mahogany'. Often I have sheltered from the rain within its flanges, watching as the torrents of water streaming down its trunk turned everything to a uniform dull grey. But somehow, when I think today of this beautiful tree, I think of it with the sun shining upon it and its bark a glowing patchwork of creams and yellows and pinks and reds and browns.

That is how I best remember it, and the old are surely entitled to linger a little where the sunshine of their memories shines the brightest.

Chapter 14

The Realm of Black Afara

Botanical Name	–	*Terminalia ivorensis*
Trade Name	–	Idigbo
Other Names	–	Framiré (Ivory Coast and France)
		Emeri (Ghana)
		Black Afara (Nigeria)
Distribution	–	Guinea to Cameroon
Timber	–	Pale yellow-brown. Grain straight to slightly wavy. Logs from some areas prone to brittle heart and thunder shakes. Dries quickly with no problems. Nails, screws and works easily.
Commercial Uses	–	Furniture, high class joinery, decorative veneers.

IN THE AFRICA of my day no colonials clung to their national identity as jealously and as proudly as did the English. Very few of
them made more than the most token effort to integrate with this
savage part of the world to which they had come so willingly and
with such eager anticipation. Only too quickly did the euphoria
wear off as they found themselves succumbing to the suffocating,
sweltering humidity, to the usual bitter denunciations of what they
considered to be the doltish indolence and apathy of 'the natives',
and to the inevitable seductive call of the gin bottle.

The standard English traditions were maintained throughout.
Their monarch's birthday was a time for loyal toasts to be offered
and Empire Day was a day for the Union Flag to be proudly raised
at expatriate clubs and private dwellings. Hot tea, dispensed in
'proper' English china, was partaken of a 4 p.m. sharp, no matter
how enervatingly stifling the conditions, and in the most remote of
outposts the bachelor expatriate would don a freshly ironed white
shirt and tie as he sat down to his solitary dinner each evening, even
though he knew that there was not one single white man within a
hundred square miles of him to appreciate the formality. The true
British colonial would not have had it otherwise. There were standards to maintain, even though only his African servant was there to
see that he was maintaining those standards.

No time of the year was looked forward to more than the
Christmas period. The fact that the Festive Season fell during the
hottest time of the year on the Coast did not dissuade the true Brit
from sticking inflexibly to all the niceties that Christmas in 'civilized' lands meant to him or her. Those gramophone records that
had not melted in the heat during the preceding year were dusted
down and the dulcet tones of Bing Crosby would come drifting
lazily over the compound to compete – generally unsuccessfully –
with the harsh squawks of the hornbills in the umbrella trees.
Scrawny turkeys – surprisingly common in even the more remote of
stations – were *de rigueur* for the Christmas Day dinner while, in
the larger expatriate clubs, Santas boiled under their heavy red
robes as they handed out the Christmas gifts to the European
progeny.

One major difficulty experienced was in the procuring of some kind of bush that looked even remotely like the traditional idea of a Christmas tree. While, during a much later era, artificial Christmas trees were being sold in the big expatriate stores in the major towns, back in those days it could be quite a problem, even in up-country stations where one was surrounded by trees. Conifers just did not grow in the African bush.

There was, however, one useful substitute for those who happened to live in the right area – the young of the black afara tree. Black afara was by no means a conifer and its leaves were certainly not what one would expect of a Christmas tree, but it served the purpose, for it was exactly the right shape. In its formative years the branches are whorled in the most regularly storied layers around the stem, in precisely the same way as those of a Norway spruce, the traditional European Christmas tree. Like the spruce, its branches are firm yet springy, ideal for hanging the tinsel and baubles upon, and it has the advantage over its European equivalent in that its leaves are a lot easier to sweep up when they fall on the carpet.

The black afara is a large tree, occurring in both the ever-green and the drier zones of the rainforests. It can grow to a height of 45 metres and a diameter of 1.50 metres. When young, it is straight of stem from ground level up; in maturity, it develops heavy surface roots and basal swellings. The characteristic whorled and storied formation of the branches in young trees gradually disappears with age as the branches begin to get heavier and sweep downwards. The bright-green leaves are about 8 centimetres long, obovate, and formed in tufts at the ends of the branchlets. They are usually shed during the months of mid-January to end March, the new growth starting in April. The inflorescences are tiny but so numerous on their long fragile stalks that the crown of the tree is splashed with washes of pale yellow among the green of the leaves in the flowering season just as the rains are commencing. By contrast with this relative gaiety, the deeply grooved bark is of a sombre dusty black colour, this characteristic having earned it the sobriquet of 'black afara' from Nigerian tree-finders in the early days of forestry

165

prospecting, the closely related 'white afara', or *Terminalia superba*, having a silvery-white bark.

The fruit is an oval nut 2 centimetres long situated in the centre of a transparent wing 6 centimetres in length. It is edible, and it is avidly eaten by a variety of forest creatures. Annual production is copious, and, on forest clearings and along the sides of old logging roads regeneration can be prolific. Some favoured areas can be almost completely dominated by this species. It coppices freely, too, and because it is a very fast grower, it has long been a favourite for regeneration programmes by the Forest Departments of a number of countries along the Coast.

Its timber has long been a favourite with the export trade, too. The name by which the trade refers to afara timber depends largely upon which side of the English Channel the buyer hails from. The British call it 'idigbo', while on the mainland of Europe they call it 'framiré'. (The name 'black afara' refers to the standing tree.) The timber has a decided greenish hue when the tree is fresh felled, but it soon changes to its familiar tawny yellow on exposure to sunlight. It has been used from time to time as a substitute for plain oak, mainly because of the colour resemblance and its vaguely similar grain formation. In addition, mechanical tests have shown it to be as strong and as stiff as English oak in bending properties, albeit a lot softer and less resistant to shock loads than the oak. Timber from trees growing in the drier parts of the semi-deciduous zone has a strong tendency towards brittle-heart and thunder shakes, and those defects are usually marked by a very distinct shade of pink on the log face. Timber from sound trees, though, is surprisingly durable, and it works easily and well with all manner of tools.

It is very popular in Europe nowadays as a general utility timber, from rotary-cut veneers to plywood to virtually all manner of interior and exterior carpentry. There are certain drawbacks, however. The timber contains a yellow colouring substance which can stain fabrics, and it has acidic properties which, in moist conditions, have a tendency to corrode any ferrous metals in contact with it.

Black afara is one large tree of the African rainforests which has a relatively short lifespan. It grows with astonishing rapidity, then,

166

having attained its goal of maturity, it seems to settle back and await its fate, adopting with unseemly haste all the tree ailments associated with old age and dying. This is particularly so with trees growing in conditions that are either too wet or too dry for them. A grossly swollen butt is a sure indicator that the rot has started, metaphorically and physically, within the bole, and it is one symptom of aging that will spread rapidly throughout the length of the tree, first in the form of brittle-heart and associated fungal streaks, then degenerating into a full-scale heart rot.

It is a tree that is very susceptible to the effects of early rain season storms. Trees – especially those whose butts have been weakened by disease – fall readily, and fallen trees are usually pitsawn by locals; being easily sawn, its timber is valued for any manner of things. In the old days the bark was boiled to obtain a yellow dye, and a decoction of it was widely used as an antiseptic for cuts and abrasions.

There is one other tree which, in the early stages of growth, bears a close resemblance to the black afara because of its black, vertically-grooved bark. The makoré (*Tieghemella heckelii*) grows into a true forest giant, attaining heights and diameters that black afara can never achieve, and in maturity there can be no mistaking the two. Not only does the makoré dominate all around it with its sheer size, but there is a special beauty about it that one does not normally associate with enormity. It can reach a height of 55 metres and a diameter of 2.5 metres. It usually only has thick surface roots and butt flares, and the trunk is generally very straight and cylindrical. It is by no means a common tree, and, like the black afara, it avoids the wetter parts of the rainforest. However, where it is encountered, one will usually find not just one specimen standing on its own but a little group of up to half a dozen trees, almost certainly indicating that its large hard seed stones have been deposited there at some time in the distant past by wandering families of elephants. The pink inner bark slowly exudes a sticky white latex to which elephants seem to be attracted, for they will gouge away the hard, black, dead outer bark with their tusks in order to tear this juicy inner fibre off with their trunks in long strips.

Even more attractive to the elephants are the fruits of this tree. Scientists call this fruit a 'berry', but anything less like a berry you are never likely to see in your life. It resembles nothing so much as a large (10 centimetres by 8 centimetres) bright-yellow ovoid mango, which usually contains a couple of large (5 centimetres by 3 centimetres) and very hard seeds. Fruit production can be copious in favourable years. Village women gather the fruits by the basketful and wash off the fleshy pulp, leaving a sticky substance which is used as a glue for catching rodents for the pot. The hard seed shells are very rich in fat, and they are broken open, dried, then battered to a paste in stone mortars. The paste is then boiled and the fat which floats to the surface is strained off and used as a cooking oil. Although slightly yellowish in hue, it is quite without flavour of any kind and it makes a superb cooking oil. In some parts the tree is protected from timber companies by the people who live in the forest for this very reason.

The timber from makoré is much prized by the export trade, similar as it is in many respects to mahogany. It varies in colour from pink to blood-red or a dark reddish-brown, occasionally showing a most attractive chequered figure. Its favourable qualities compare to American mahogany, and the wood is extremely durable. The furniture manufacturers of Europe particularly value it for producing a high quality sliced veneer.

Makoré has two major drawbacks, however: mature trees are so heavy that particularly large specimens are inclined to shatter badly on felling, while during conversion in sawmilling the very fine sawdust can seriously affect the nose, eyes, throat and skin.

Another interesting species which I have often found scattered throughout areas frequented by black afara is the kanda tree (*Beilschmiedia mannii*). Kanda is not, by any stretch of the imagination, a species that is inclined to excite the mind of the average log exporter, although it is true to say that very small quantities of its timber have been shipped from time to time. Indeed, the wood is not even of very much interest to the indigenous African. A fallen tree might be turned into planks or made into a canoe by him, but his main interest in the tree is for other reasons than construction.

Kanda rarely grows to great heights. Occasional trees may be found at heights of around 30 metres and 0.50 metres in diameter, but not often. More generally, it is an inconspicuous tree of the middle storey of the forest. The bole is straight and slender, with low sharp buttresses, and the bark is of an anonymous greyish-green hue. The crown is small and very dense. Even the flowers are inconspicuous, being tiny, light-green and hidden from view amidst the bottle-green darkness of the leaves. The large dark-red fruits, when they appear in the early part of the dry season, seem equally to fade into nothingness against this drab background.

Yet the tree hides a secret. Crush the leaves in your hand and a most beautiful aroma instantly wafts up your nostrils. It is an aroma that will still be with you after you have washed your hands several times. Cut a slash with your machete in the thin bark and you will find that the same fragrance is with you, only much stronger this time: a sort of combination of cedarwood, sandalwood, wych-hazel, star anise, lemon blossom, with traces of all the perfumes of ancient Araby to boot.

Kanda timber is actually quite pleasing in appearance. It is a dark reddish-brown, and it, too, is very fragrant. Unlike many timbers which exude pleasant scents while being sawn, only to lose them in the drying process, kanda timber retains its fragrance even after being sawn and dried. Many years ago, when I was in a position to carry out sawmill experiments on a large number of comparatively unknown African rainforest species, I was rather puzzled as to why the timber trade had never shown much interest in this species as a possible substitute for mahogany. One probable clue came after a number of simple tests: the timber had a high silica content and, as a result, was very rough on the saw teeth. In addition, it was found to be very difficult to dry and subject in the drying process to a most annoying case-hardening. However, once it had been successfully dried, the wood planed and moulded well, took a beautiful finish, and it held nails and screws. When, some time later, I was able to study the logs in a plymill situation, they seemed to slice and peel satisfactorally, and the timber was reported to be very durable.

All parts of the tree seem to contain aromatic oil glands. The fragrant seeds are edible: they are dried and crushed in mortars and are used to thicken stews and pepper-sauces. The fragrant flowers are much sought when they appear during the last few months of the dry season. These are beaten up with rice and cooked, imparting a most delicious flavour to the whole meal. Perhaps not surprisingly, oil extracted from the particularly fragrant roots is much used by maidens wishing to draw attention to their otherwise modest charms, while young blades heading out of bush for a night or two on the town consider themselves to be completely irresistable with a goodly splash of the unique kanda perfume distributed around those parts of their bodies they hold most dear to them.

*   *   *   *   *

ALONG WITH ITS close relatives the rock and bush hyrax, the tree hyrax has been in Africa for some 40 million years. It is a curious creature, rather like a guinea pig in appearance, and indeed the early scientists linked it to the guinea pig. Today the world of science considers it to be more closely related to the elephant and the aardvark, but anything less like either of those two would be hard to imagine.

The tree hyrax, as its name indicates, is mainly arboreal. Its preferred home is in the upper reaches of the highest trees available in its locality. The crown of the black afara suits it just fine, forming as it does a concealing black umbrella over its activities, diurnal and nocturnal. It will usually come down to the lower branches, or even to the ground, as necessity demands on its quest for food, but it prefers the safety afforded by the tall trees. It looks just like a large rodent – almost beaver-like – and it is about 50 centimetres in length and 30 centimetres in height. Its fur is thick and very soft, dark grey on the back and with a light grey underbelly. Its ears are short and rounded and its legs are very short. The feet are long, with thick curved nails, and the soles have a rubbery feel to them, with tiny ridges for gripping branches. It is as secure in its movements among the high tops as any monkey, and the greyness of its coat makes it all but invisible to the hunter.

A curious feature of the hyrax family is the broad dorsal gland which it exposes when it is excited, afraid or angry. It turns its back on the object of its concern and the white hairs around the gland stiffen and part. It eats leaves, fruit, twigs and bark, and it requires very little water, the efficacy of its kidneys being such that it can survive on a very low moisture intake for long periods.

The tree hyrax, however, is not confined to the realm of the black afara. It is, in fact, to be seen almost anywhere one is liable to find trees south of the Sahara. In the absence of trees, it may even be found living among holes in rocks above the normal tree line, the East Zaire volcanoes and Mount Cameroon being good examples. But its natural habitat is high among the branches, and it was while I was living briefly in an area of high forest dominated by black afara in eastern Nigeria that I derived the most poignant memories of this strange animal. Here, the woods surrounding my house echoed to their calls every night. Just after dark, night after night, their cries would commence, to continue on and on and on, then stopping as suddenly as they had started, only for the racket to start up again in the middle of the night, as though they were determined that, because they were not in the mood of slumber, nothing else in the forest should be allowed to sleep either. There is no other call remotely like the call of the hyrax. It is a rattling cry that can be heard many miles away, and it is quite blood-curdling – sometimes described as being like that of a child being throttled slowly by an exasperated parent. Each individual call lasts about five minutes, but before it has ended another hyrax joins in, then another picks up the chorus, then another, then another, until the night air all through the dark woods throbs to this eerie sound that is so uniquely African.

Leopards and pythons hunt the hyrax, as do human beings, for its flesh is good to eat. They also make very affectionate pets; too affectionate, as I was to find out, for I was for a short time the reluctant foster parent to half a dozen of them. When I was in the house they followed me everywhere, running behind me in single file, squeaking and twittering contentedly. They were a constant hazard, for one was always tripping over them, and when my cook once practically parboiled himself with a pan of scalding water, they were banned from the kitchen.

Each evening they were locked in a little kitchen annexe. Just after dark, on cue, their contact calls would start up, and a horrendous racket would reverberate over the whole compound, continuing for the next couple of hours or so, each animal seeming to vie with the others for the title of Africa's noisiest creature. Around 3 o'clock in the morning, just when one was at last dropping off to sleep, the night air would once again be split by their din. It was often hard to imagine that a creature not much bigger than a domestic cat could make such a row, and it was with considerable relief that, after enduring this chorus for several months, I was able to offload the whole hyrax menagerie on to a noted itinerant zoo collector.

*   *   *   *   *

I WAS STANDING at the edge of a large clearing in the Guiglo region of the Ivory Coast. Before me was a sea of sawgrass, the viciously serrated strands just waiting for the unwary to attempt passage. Behind me was the coolness of the forest I had just walked through.

The sky was of that faded washed-blue so familiar to all who have lived through a West African harmattan season. Directly in front some scattered regeneration of black afara was making a valiant attempt to force its way through the rampant tangles of vegetation. The trees were of various sizes, from knee-high to about head height. One beautifully shaped specimen towered above the rest to a height of 4 metres, its regularly whorled branches in perfect equidistant spacing around the stem.

A flicker of Lincoln-green near the top of the tree caught my attention. A pair of lovebirds were feeding on something or other and, strain my eyes though I might against the glare of the sun, I could not make out what it was. I watched the two charming little parrots for a time, afraid to move lest they take fright. Unlike any of the species of lovebird most favoured by cage-bird enthusiasts, these were rather plain in appearance. They did not have the more generally accepted red beaks and orange heads of their cousins and their silvery-grey beaks and black and white neck bands were the only variation to the delicate shades of green that clothed them entirely.

A sharp metallic 'chack' rang out, and one of the pair flew off into the adjacent forest. I thought that perhaps he had seen me, but he returned seconds later with a large sprig of bright-red fruit in his beak. The pair began to eat again. I knew now what was on their menu: bush cherries. I had been walking all morning through the forest behind me, and it was a forest almost entirely dominated by large afaras and small slender bush cherry trees. I had stopped frequently to eat the fruit, and nowhere else in all my African travels had I seen them in such profusion.

The bush cherry (*Maesobotrya barteri*) is, in appearance, nothing much to write home about, being very much an under-storey tree. It has a skinny and very knobbly stem, and its bark is a perfectly anonymous dull-green hue. Its timber is of very little use for anything, even for firewood, because it is as fragile as cardboard and prey to every insect and fungal agency in Africa. But, for the inhabitants of the forest, its uses are many.

There are two varieties. One, *M. barteri var. barteri*, has dark purple berries, while the other, *M. barteri var. sparsiflora*, has bright-red berries. Both are succulent and both are eaten by many forest creatures, including humans, but my own preference is for the latter, for not only is their taste delightfully tart but they are most refreshing when one comes across them on one's travels in the humidity of the forest.

The berries grow in small clumps all the way up the slender stem during the early part of the dry season. They ripen quickly from bright green to the familiar shiny red cherry colour, and by mid-November they are ready for eating. The thin and rather stringy bark of the tree is sweet and considered edible. It is chewed for a variety of reasons, mainly for the treatment of ailments associated with the digestive system and the urinary tract. In the Ivory Coast the sap is taken by those stricken by jaundice to alleviate their suffering, and it is also considered to have haemostatic properties.

I am told that the fruit of both varieties makes very good jam. I have never seen or tasted the jam, but I am sure it must be good, for bush cherries are my own personal favourites. None of the fruits cultivated by man come even close to them in my esteem.

One of the lovebirds had returned with another large bunch of cherries, and the two were now eating contentedly on the topmost branch of the young black afara. They were rather careless feeders, and small sprigs of discarded cherries dangled from the branch below where they were perched. The little bush cherries looked for all the world like holly berries as they hung there, glinting scarlet in the late morning sunshine.

I turned to go. The sun was climbing high overhead here in the tropics, the bush cherries were out in their fullness and sweetness, and far, far away in Europe Christmas was just around the corner.

Chapter 15

The Naga Trees of Putu

Botanical Name   –   *Brachystegia spp.*

Trade Name   –   Naga

Other Names   –   Okwen (Nigeria)
Meblo (Ivory Coast)
Poli (Liberia)

Distribution   –   West Africa, from Liberia to Nigeria.

Timber   –   Light-brown, often with alternating golden-brown and dark-brown stripes. Only moderately durable. Easy to work with machine tools; difficult with hand tools.

Commercial Uses   –   General construction; plywood and veneer.

'THE SILVER BIRCH is a dainty lady,' proclaimed an evocative poet once upon a time. I have to admit that I, too, have always had a tendency to think of certain tree species in human terms, to think of them as being either masculine or feminine, even to regard some as being little more than gender benders, of little obvious practical use to anyone or anything – just trees that seem to have been put on this earth of ours solely for the purpose of relieving the monotony of all the green around them with their splashes of outrageous gaiety.

Naga, though, is no gender bender. This is a masculine tree, if ever there was one. Naga would be the Mike Tyson of my tree world any time. It is a great, burly, thick-armed brute of a tree that totally dominates the forest around it, to the extent that little else is permitted to survive in its awesome presence. In maturity, there can be few more impressive sights. Often reaching 45 metres in height and surpassing 2 metres in diameter, its bole is cylindrical, scaly of bark, and devoid of branches up to the topmost 6 metres, at which point a few massive limbs suddenly sprawl out flatly and almost at right-angles to form an umbrella of branches and foliage. The 'umbrella' analogy is given added emphasis by the characteristic drooping habit of the twigs and leaves around the perimeter of the crown.

Despite its huge size, naga has a rather open crown. There is a reason for this: in form, and in its lack of density, the foliage of naga is not unlike that of the European ash, so sunlight filters through with relative ease to form pretty patterns on the ground below. One might have expected, therefore, to find plant life in abundance around the tree itself, but this is not always the case. At the end of each rain season, between the months of August and September, naga suddenly sheds all its leaves. Considering the fecund humidity of the climate, these leaves take a surprising length of time to decompose, forming instead a thick black leathery carpet around the tree, which appears to have a considerable inhibitory effect upon most forms of plant regeneration. This applies equally to its own seed, though naga will regenerate freely in parts where the soil has been disturbed.

Naga is a tree of the evergreen forests; within the limit of its distribution range, it may be found on a great variety of sites, although essentially it is a lowland tree. Tolerant of hillsides and even steeply sloping ground, it is not fond of ridges or high tops. Nor does it like swampy conditions or sites that are periodically inundated.

Considering the tree's outward magnificence, I have always thought of its timber as being rather disappointing. The forest African, for example, did not make the use of it that one might have expected, even in those areas in which the tree grew in abundance. For one thing, in maturity the tree was just too big to handle. In addition, he found that the timber, though only moderately hard, was rough in texture and surprisingly difficult to work. It was cross-grained and had quite a severe blunting effect on the teeth of saws. Even when the tree was young enough, and might have been of a diameter suitable for the making of canoes, naga was rarely utilized even for this purpose. A major drawback was that all naga, irrespective of age and size, had a tendency to ring-shake severely on felling. Another problem was that in young trees the ratio of sapwood to heartwood was high, naga sapwood being extremely susceptible to attack by all kinds of boring insects from the moment the tree hit the ground.

Trees of suitable diameter were occasionally felled near villages to pitsaw into rough planks for rafters, beams or crude furniture, but, because of all the defects associated with it, the timber tended to be a secondary choice for the man of the forest. Indeed, there were a few tribes who referred to it as the 'Poor Man's Timber'.

This was precisely the attitude of the white man to it when he first came on the scene. It was not to be until the late 1960's, when costs of exporting the old traditional species began to soar all over the Coast and the search began for cheaper types of utility plywood, that naga started to come into its own. By this time, too, machines and equipment in both the logging and sawmill industries had become much bigger and more sophisticated, and log size and weight was no longer the problem it had once been.

177

Controversially, this was one species of which the loggers could claim, with some justification, that their activities were actually of some help in ensuring its survival. Regeneration, they would point out, was invariably prolific along the verges of old logging roads and around the stumps of parent trees after felling. The topsoil, once disturbed, almost immediately sprouted new life. Environmentalists would no doubt reply that – left to its own devices – regeneration would eventually flourish around the base of the living tree by a much more acceptable method. Peripadetic families of elephants are fond of resting up under it on hot afternoons, churning up the ground with their digging and their frolicking.

Naga, though, is not a tree that depends upon the company of its own kind. Only twice during my wanderings have I found single dominant stands of naga. Given conditions in which it finds itself with sufficient elbow room to allow its great crown to develop fully, it mixes well and freely with other species. Indeed, it is much more often to be found scattered singly or in pairs, in mixture with others, than in groups of its own kind.

The type of company it keeps is usually dependant upon the topographic and climatic conditions in which it grows. Where it makes its home around creeks and rivers in the central belt of the evergreen forests, the oil-bean tree (*Pentaclethra macrophylla*) will often be found in the vicinity.

The oil-bean tree is a curious tree to find among the ramrod-straight perfections of its better-known companions. Although it can grow to a substantial height – up to 30 metres in optimum conditions – it is almost always a rather ugly and misshapen tree, low-forking and branchy, and of not the slightest interest to the commercial logger. Around the beginning of the 20th century a few logs of the species were tried out in the Liverpool market under the hopeful euphemism of 'African Greenheart', but this was an experiment that – like so many involving West African timbers in those early years – got no further than the first sawmill. The timber was just too hard, too heavy, and too coarse of grain to interest the lumber man, regardless of whatever fancy *nom-de-plume* its importers might have felt like attaching to it.

To the African, the real attraction of the oil-bean tree lay in its many uses in food and in medicine. From February to April a glowing mantle of fragrant pale-yellow flowers covered its dense dark-green crown. By September, long woody pods had developed, each one containing around half-a-dozen large, hard-shelled, purplish beans. It was at this time that what sounded like a minor war would erupt in the forest, for the pods would dehisce in a veritable cannonade of sound, pistol shots of explosions that would send the seeds tumbling to the ground below in constant showers.

When villagers had an oil-bean tree growing in the vicinity, they would clear away all undergrowth from around it in order to facilitate collection of its fruit, for the pleasantly fragrant beans were very rich in proteins. The beans were usually roasted or boiled before being eaten, but they were also ground in mortars for use as flavouring in stews. In the old days – perhaps even now in the more remote areas – oil beans were traded wherever there happened to be a village market.

It was not only for its beans that this tree was regarded with particular affection by the forest African. A number of common ailments were treated with potions obtained from the sap and the bark, and they also played a part in treatment of deformities of the spine. The oil-bean tree almost always had a large and distinctive hump halfway up the trunk, and this was widely believed to have been put there by the gods of the forest as an omen for the bush doctor. A piece of bark was removed from the living tree as near to the hump as possible by repeated beating with a stone or club. The bark was then pounded to a mush in a mortar and mixed with clay from the mound of the forest termite, the resultant poultice being spread on the back of the patient. Anyone suffering from mysterious swellings on any other part of the body would be treated in the same way.

While it was mainly for its bountiful harvest that the oil-bean tree received the special protection of the people of the forest, it may not, alas, always be so. Their children, like children the world over, may soon turn their backs on the old ways, once they have savoured the gastronomic delights of their first hamburgers. But so long as there are still a few isolated pockets left of Africa's ancient rain-forests, the oil-bean tree will, for a time, remain. There is no money in it for anyone, other than for those who gather its produce in unspoilt places.

Even in the world of trees, it sometimes pays to be a plain jane.

*   *   *   *   *

NAGA AND I go back a long way. It was the first of the truly great forest giants I ever encountered in Africa. In fact, for a time I lived with two of them.

I was on my first tour on the Coast, where I had been posted to a station in the heart of the Ondo forests in Nigeria. It was a little isolated (my nearest white neighbour – my boss – lived about 45 miles to the south over a laterite logging road) but, as I have always rather enjoyed my own company, this suited me fine.

The location was beautiful. The Oni River swept regally past the foot of the compound on its way to the Bight of Benin. In the rains, the Oni, like most tropical rivers, was a formidable roiling torrent that carried all before it, including, on occasion, my only link with the outside world – the long wooden bridge that spanned it fifty yards upstream from my house. In the dry season, however, it was as pretty a little river as you could hope to find anywhere in the world, a bubbling placid waterway strewn with boulders and with deep pools full of catfish and tigerfish.

In December, the whole length of the river bank at the foot of my compound would suddenly become an orange glow of harmattan lilies, planted there God knows when by some long-gone colonial. Just downstream from my house, at the end of the compound, was a large grove of grapefruit, oranges, avocados and bananas, planted there too, presumably, by the same anonymous colonial. My grape-fruit and avocados were renowned for being without equal in the whole of Nigeria.

Across the river from my compound lay the forest. From the verandah of the house one could see only thorny thickets of understorey bush, with the occasional scraggy ebony jutting through the tangle, but about thirty metres downstream and in full view of the house were two colossal nagas, one on each side of the river and growing directly opposite one another.

They were magnificent specimens. Their great limbs spread out over the river, joining hands far above the fast flowing waters. In common with most of the species, their branches were covered with epiphytes and ferns, and long ropes of liane trailed down to the ground from the topmost parts of them. A pair of fish eagles used the two trees as a periodic base for their activities, their shrill cries echoing back across my compound from the wall of the forest as they cruised up and down over the water in their ceaseless quest for food.

It was always at the height of the dry season each year that the pestiferous little guenon monkeys came in from the east. They swarmed over the river in hordes, up to thirty in each troupe, and they came with only one purpose in mind – to raid my grove of fruit trees. Across the natural bridge created by the linking of the naga branches high over the water they came, chattering and leaping and dancing and swinging, to abseil swiftly down the long liana ropes to the ground and disappear among the bananas on my side. They were extremely wasteful creatures. When they got tired of eating, they would sling oranges and avocados and lumps of pawpaw at each other, like mischievous children who had glutted themselves in the vicar's orchard and were now out to create as much havoc as possible before departing. I tried everything to discourage them, even to the extent of hiring a man from the nearby village to sit among the fruit trees by day to scare them off with sticks and stones. It was useless. Either my guard would fall asleep in the heat of the day when all self-respecting monkeys should have been asleep as well, or they simply hurled his missiles right back at him, with greater force and certainly greater accuracy. Finally, succumbing with the utmost reluctance to the pleas of the villagers – whose banana patches were also suffering from the activities of the little horrors – I shot two of them in the hope that this would show their friends the error of their ways.

181

The others got the message, all right – for approximately forty-eight hours. Within two days they were back in even greater numbers and I left them to it.

I have never shot a monkey since that day. The sight of those two broken bodies lying on their backs in the cool shadows of the citrus trees, dead eyes staring up at me, would have melted the heart of a wooden god.

So what if they did steal my fruit? It was, after all, but poor reward for the entertainment they gave me every Sunday as I sat on my verandah watching their antics high up in those two great nagas by the banks of the beautiful Oni River.

*   *   *   *   *

SEVERAL THOUSAND MILES to the west and a quarter of a century later I was again to be associated with naga in a memorable way. This time I was working in high forest just to the west of the Putu Range in Liberia. Naga was very much the dominant species here, and this particular area was the most agreeable of forests in which to operate, for the undergrowth was sparse. Indeed, there were places where the regeneration under the trees was of such sparsity as to make walking through this naga forest as easy and as enjoyable as a stroll through an English beech wood in the early spring.

It was particularly pleasant during the harmattan. The beginning of the harmattan about mid-November seemed to signal the start of all kinds of activity around the treetops. The morning sun had no sooner dispersed the cool mists of night than the naga seedpods (about half the size of those of the oil-bean tree) began to crackle and pop and bang, releasing their hard little brown beans to drop in a steady pitter-pattering drizzle of sound to the ground below. Orioles gave occasional flashes of their golden glory in the gloom, and the unmistakable hollow WHOO-HOOP-HOOP-HOOP-HOOP of the migrant hoopoe rang constantly through the trees. The skies were an azure delight in the aftermath of the rains as flocks of grey parrots and little green pigeons wheeled tirelessly overhead, the parrots whistling and calling endlessly to each other, the pigeons silent of voice but with a WHISSH upon WHISSH of fast-beating wings as each flight soared over.

Here I had my first real encounter with the most extraordinary bird it has ever been my good fortune to see. I had seen touracos from time to time throughout the rainforests of Africa but never had I seen them in such abundance as in this place. For reasons that remain something of a mystery to me, this strange bird seemed to have a particular predilection towards the naga trees of Putu. Here they performed their quaint rituals high up in the tall trees, bowing their heads at each other like gaudily-painted geishas during a night out on the town, and here they mated and nested and reared their odd little chicks.

In fact, everything about this bird is odd. It is exclusively African, and it is related to the cuckoo, though – to this layman's eye at least – anything less like the European cuckoo would be hard to imagine. In flight, it looks the most prehistoric of birds as it flips and flops laboriously from tree to tree, reminding one of old black-and-white movies of stick-and-canvas pterodactyls in flight over forbidding landscapes on a Hollywood back lot.

The word 'touraco' embraces a considerable number of related species, the estimate appearing to vary according to whichever book one happens to consult on the subject. A few of the species are savannah dwellers, but those are grey and almost dowdy by comparison with their rainforest cousins.

The touracos of the forest vary in size from about that of a rook to the size of a cock pheasant. They eat many different kinds of fruit – most commonly figs – and leaves, buds and flowers of a variety of tree species. They are essentially arboreal, generally to be seen only when loping along the great orchid-covered limbs in the forest gallery like demented Groucho Marxes in pursuit of feminine company. They are not enthusiastic fliers, preferring to glide from tree to tree wherever possible.

I have seen their nests on a number of occasions, always after loggers had felled the trees in which they had been built. They are just like much larger versions of the nests of the common wood pigeon, consisting of a flimsy platform of twigs laid perilously on top of branches in the crowns of the tallest trees, and usually containing two whiteish eggs.

Touracos are secretive, but very social, and they are very noisy indeed, communicating in loud choruses of harsh barks and grunts. One is aware of the presence of touracos in a patch of forest long before one enters it.

As the name might indicate, their heads are usually crested, the crests often tipped with red or white. Their bills are usually thickly stubby and small, but it is for their plumage that touracos first raised the eyebrows of the boffins in the world of science.

The plumage of nearly all the forest touracos has a loose and rather fluffy appearance to it at first sight, but closer inspection shows it to have an almost metallic lustre to it, with iridescent deep blues, violets and greens. One of the things that makes this bird so special in ornithological societies is the fact that the wonderful green coloration in its feathers is produced by a substance which has been named '*turacoverdin*', and this is the only green pigment known to occur in birds. Equally interesting is the fact that the dazzling red of their wing patches is caused by turacin, a copper-bearing pigment that is also unique among birds and is easily removed from the feathers by soaking in a chemical solution.

In the forest fringes bordering the Putu Range, I encountered a much larger species of touraco. This was *Corythaeola cristata*, or the Great Blue Touraco, which was about the size of a peacock, and indeed this was the name given to it by the people of Putu. Unlike the others, the great blue had no red feathers on its wings, but its plumage was of the deepest, richest blue I have ever seen on any living creature. Like its smaller cousins, it built its spartan nest high up in the forest canopy. This touraco was not in the slightest reclusive, although I found it no easier to spot than the others in the gloom of the treetops. However, its feeding habits made the great blue much easier to study than the others. Its main diet appeared to consist of the fruit, buds, flowers and young shoots of the ubiquitous umbrella tree (*Musanga cecropioides*), a tree that grew in profusion wherever one happened upon an open glade, clearing or old disused road in the rainforests. Around the Putu crags there were plenty of open spaces, so the umbrella tree was particularly abundant in this area. As the umbrella tree was never more than a spindly stick of a tree, seldom reaching above 8 metres in height, the great blue touraco had to descend from the high tops rather more often than most of the other members of its family in order to feed.

The great blue touracos were even noisier than the others. They made an incredible din, and when one started up, it was a signal for every other touraco in the vicinity to join in the chorus – a jarring KOW-KOW-KOW-KOW-KORUK-KORUK-KORUK-KORUK racket that would clatter out over the trees and rattle among the crags of Putu as the birds made their long glide down to the thickets of umbrella trees far below them.

I regret to report that I have, from time to time, eaten touraco, though I have never done so with any degree of enthusiasm. Without exception, I have found their flesh to be black and stringy and bitter and rather horrible, and this is one African delicacy that I do not ever expect to find featuring regularly on the menus of the better hotels in London and Paris.

Touracos, I am told on good authority, make fine aviary birds. That may be so, and any system that guarantees their survival has got to be lauded. I have never seen them in a cage, aviary or zoo, and I rather hope that I never shall. To my mind, touracos belong only where I remember them best, in the rainforests of Africa.

*   *   *   *   *

INCREASINGLY, AS I grow older, there are times – especially when the cold English rain comes slanting in from the North Sea and over the bare lands of winter – that my thoughts drift back over the years and I am listening once more to the cracking of hard woody pods on green-capped ghostly nagas, and the still heat of the African day is with me again, the air is full of the patter of seeds falling to earth around me. It is at times like these that I hear, yet again, the haunting cries of those strange primordial birds as they scuttle along on their mysterious ways among the orchids where the roof of the forest meets the blue of the sky in far-off lands at a time when the world was young and I was younger.

God's Heaven must be made of dreams such as those.

Chapter 16

Monkey Can't Climb

Botanical Name	–	*Distemonanthus benthamianus*
Trade Name	–	Movingui
Other Names	–	Barré (Ivory Coast) Anyan (Nigeria) Oguéminia (Gabon)
Distribution	–	Sierra Leone to Zaire
Timber	–	Yellow. Grain wavy, interlocked, producing beautifully mottled figuring when quarter-sawn. Hard and heavy. Works well with all tools but planing sometimes difficult. Must be pre-bored for nails. Excellent finish.
Commercial Uses	–	High quality cabinet and furniture making. Decorative sliced veneer and marquetry.

NEARLY EVERYTHING ABOUT the movingui is unusual, right down to, and including, its scientific name, *Distemonanthus benthamianus*. In fact, it could perhaps be asserted with some degree of accuracy that the '*benthamianus*' part of its Sunday name is the only conventional thing about this tree. George Bentham was a staid old English botanist of the 19th century who would no doubt have been delighted to learn that his surname was to be attached for all posterity to one of the most brightly cheerful-looking trees in all of Africa, but perhaps less than enamoured to be told that the noble family name of Bentham was to be appended to the Greek '*Distemonanthus*', a term rather loosely translated as 'flower with two phalluses'.

Movingui is an almost startlingly beautiful tree. Although it was by no means common anywhere even in my day, it was more usually encountered in areas of secondary forest or in the drier, more northerly parts of the high forest than in the southern evergreen forests. Never huge in size, movingui trees growing in the high forest were generally of greater dimensions than those in secondary forest and could reach heights of around 30 metres and diameters of 0.70 centimetres, but seldom more than that. The movingui more than made up for its modest size, however, with its sheer beauty.

Perhaps '*her* sheer beauty' would be more appropriate, for if other trees such as naga and okan and the sinister sasswood could only be termed male by virtue of their massive bulk and lack of aesthetic elegance, so, surely, must the movingui – despite the double-phallus entendre – be the most feminine looking of all trees, reminding one almost irresistibly of a favourite geisha swathed in silks of the most exotic and colourful splendour.

The bole is slender. It can occasionally be straight, but more often than not, in my experience, the top half has a gentle, graceful curve. Buttresses are generally low and rounded, although when the tree is growing in less than favourable situations – for example, in swampy hollows or on rocky hillsides – they can be quite large, sharp and widespreading. The crown is wide but very open, and the foliage is an attractive light-green. The compound leaves are reminiscent in shape and size to those of the European mountain ash. The flowers, emerging at the beginning of the dry season in October, are small but extremely pretty, with their glossy white petals and violet sepals. (This is where the 'flower with two phalluses' comes in, for the flower is equipped with two stamens, a not unusual occurrence in the strange world of botany.) Their hold on the parent tree is tenuous, and at this time of the year anyone standing underneath one will be subjected to a constant drizzle of blossoms from above. The fruits consist of paper-thin veined pods (in appearance, rather like slightly larger versions of the garden vegetable known as 'mangetout') which usually contain about 4 small seeds.

The bark, though, is what sets this tree apart from most others. It is a most extraordinary patchwork of light green, dark green, medium green, light orange, dark orange, light red, reddish-brown, grey and yellow shades. The outer bark flakes off in scales as papery-thin as the sloughed skin of a snake, leaving the new bark underneath as smooth and shiny as glass. It is for this reason that in at least two West African countries the movingui tree is known in the vernacular as 'Monkey Can't Climb'.

The timber is unusually attractive, too. When fresh-cut it is daffodil-yellow, darkening very gradually on exposure to a slightly more sombre golden-brown. It is hard and heavy, and sawing can create some problems due to concentrations of silica and gum in the wood. However, once sawn, it is reasonably easy to work with both hand and machine tools. Individual logs can produce very attractive figuring. Because of this, selected timber is reserved for conversion into sliced veneer for high-quality cabinet work, panelling and marquetry. For lower grades of timber there is also a ready market in furniture, flooring, carriage work, interior joinery and shop fittings. The timber has one major drawback, however: the cells also contain yellow deposits which, being soluble in water, can be released in suitably moist and warm conditions. It should never, therefore, be used in places like kitchens or laundries or in any situations where it is liable to be in contact with clothes or foodstuffs.

While young trees are perfectly windfirm, old trees are not. The reason is that, when they become over-mature, they are seriously affected by a form of butt-rot which rapidly leaves the first two metres or so of the bole as little more than a shell of sapwood and bark, while the rest of the bole usually remains unaffected. In my day the tree had a decided mystique about it that gave it a very high standing in the arcane world of the witchdoctor and his clientele. In addition to the 'monkey can't climb' legend, the tree had never been known to be struck by lightning. Thus, many potions were made from the living bark of the standing tree and the foliage and flowers of fallen branches for a whole host of day-to-day problems, from gruesome tribal initiation ceremonies to cures for snake-bite and protection against demons and witches. Absolute faith in the medications derived from this tree was so complete that I have known highly educated Africans seek its services via their local witchdoctor when the world of European medicine had failed them. And why not, indeed? The people of the rainforests are just as entitled to their own form of alternative medicine as anyone else.

Movingui can be found anywhere throughout the high forest, but secondary forest is where it seems to be most at home. My own most frequent encounters with it have been in the vicinity of abandoned farm clearings. Another commonly encountered species in old secondary forest of this nature is the dahoma (*Piptadeniastrum africanum*). Like the movingui, dahoma can certainly be found in the rainforests almost anywhere in tropical Africa, but again, in my experience, it is much more often encountered in areas which, in the distant past, have been cleared for cultivation, and on such sites it can form large gregarious stands. It is very much a light demander and it can grow to enormous dimensions: 45 metres high by 1.40 metres in diameter being not all that unusual.

The dahoma tree is unmistakable, but for reasons other than those which distinguish the movingui. The dahoma is a great, sprawling brute of a thing with none of the tessellate splendour of the movingui. Its bark is a leaden grey, its bole is huge and its buttresses simply enormous. Yet there is a sort of grace about it, too, when one looks at its crown from below. It is very wide-spreading, with an almost table-top flatness about it, and its fern-like leaves create a delicate filigreed pattern against the sky. It is the sort of tree beloved of Hollywood film makers when shooting scenes of the great African plains. (The range of dahoma does indeed stretch as far as the grasslands of Uganda.)

In the wetter parts of the evergreen forest the bole is usually long, cylindrical and straight, often reaching over 20 metres before branching, but in drier open areas it is much more inclined to be squat and untidy looking, forking at an unusually low level into steeply ascending thick and heavy branches which gradually taper off into long and thin branchlets. The dappled shade cast by its light ferny foliage and its very distinctive long and flat brown pods hanging down en masse from the crown made it a favourite for planting alongside avenues on Government forestry stations in the colonial era.

In January, one of the hottest and driest months of the year, the tree briefly sheds its leaves, the new leaves emerging almost immediately afterwards. These are very pretty indeed in the early stages: rose-hued, with bright-green tips. During the rains which follow, the whole crown becomes covered with a thick carpet of small yellowish flowers which have a strong smell of decay. The tree swarms with fiery red arboreal ants at this time.

First impressions are that the timber is rather unattractive, coarse and woolly and difficult to saw, and when newly sawn it is a rather unpleasant bice-green. However, it soon darkens to a uniform and quite attractive golden-brown. The fine dust that fills the air during the sawing process is a severe irritant to the eyes and lungs, and it also emits a quite appalling odour of stale urine. However, for many years the timber has maintained a certain export value as heavy-duty flooring, vehicle bodies, naval and railway construction, and work benches. In the early days it was sold as 'African greenheart', an optimistic euphemism rarely applied nowadays.

A favourite site for the growing tree is by a fast-flowing stream or river. I have two personal memories of the tree in just this sort of environment. The first is of one large and branchy specimen being felled on a stream-bank in mid-Liberia. When the chainsaw had got halfway through the trunk a veritable fountain of clear water shot out of the saw-cut and continued to pour out freely from it for some considerable time. There must have been many gallons evacuated from the tree before the flow eventually died down to a trickle. The tree was not hollow, and I could see no obvious reason for this incredible discharge of water, although the chainsaw operator – a native of the area – told me that this was a common occurrence in this area when dahoma was being felled. He said that the water was 'good medicine for malaria'. I tasted it, and found it bitter and brackish.

My second experience was in far-off Nigeria on the Anambra River, a tributary of the Niger. The bank at one point was lined with low-branching and stumpy dahoma trees, and it was here that I first noticed a characteristic peculiar also to the European beech when growing on similar sites. The long straggly branches seemed drawn down to the water surface, their ends trailing on and under the rushing water. I had been travelling downstream in a dugout canoe and, for reasons that need not detain us here, I had ended up in the river. I am no swimmer and the river was in full spate. It was an unpleasant moment, but by fortunate chance I was able to grab a slender dahoma branch and haul myself to safety.

The inoi-nut tree (*Poga oleosa*) is another whose normal habitat is the high forest but which seems to be more often seen around clearings or near villages. It is a large tree, up to 30 metres high and a metre in diameter. It rarely has any buttresses worth speaking about and its bark is smooth, greyish-green and thick. The timber is of a pinkish hue, the wide medullary rays giving it a silver-grain figure when sawn on the quarter. The export trade makes a certain amount of use of it for, although it is very soft and light, it is easily worked and attractive.

For the African, in my day at least, the main attraction of *Poga oleosa* lay not in its timber but in its fruit. The tree was particularly common in certain parts of Nigeria, where it was called the 'inoi-nut', and in areas where it was predominant one was aware of its presence wherever one went, even if one knew nothing about trees. Piles of broken shells would be seen everywhere, under trees or by the sides of bush paths or in village compounds. During the fruiting season one would frequently encounter village women sitting under trees or at the edge of farm clearings breaking the stone-hard nodose nuts. Each shell contained three oily sweet and supremely edible kernels. At this time of the year they were often for sale in village and town markets. Unwin reports that during the years of the First World War they were being sold in Calabar market at 250 for threepence, surely the bargain of the century for this delicacy.

To readers of certain vintage, the camwood tree will need no introduction. Anyone who has ever read a 'Boy's Own Adventure' tale knows about the camwood dye, even if he was a little hazy as to how it was produced. 'The natives stole silently through the swamps in their war canoes, their faces dyed with camwood . . .' was a familiar enough cliché to those of us reared on a diet of those delightful tales during the 1930s.

There are two distinctly different types of camwood. The timber trade's original was *Baphia nitida*, while the other – labelled 'false camwood' – was *Pterocarpus soyauxii*, nowadays called 'African padauk'. Both are small, low-branching, understorey trees, and both produce the famous blood-red dye. Both are of the greatest juju significance because of this fact and because of the dye's connection with West Africa's more violent feuds in ages past. Both species could often be found planted near to villages or around farm enclaves. It is only when the tree is quite old that the familiar deep-red heartwood appears in *Baphia nitida*, and even then the heartwood is only very small in diameter. That of the padauk is in much larger proportions. *Baphia nitida*, the 'true camwood', is hard to come by nowadays, and nearly all export material is from the padauk. Anyway, who in the timber trade cares? The timber of padauk is just as highly regarded by their customers, for it is durable, works extremely well, has quite outstanding stability, and takes a most beautiful finish. As a result, it is used for high-class joinery, fancy turnery, gun stocks, heavy-duty flooring, decorative tool handles and agricultural implements, to name but a few. Selected logs are reserved for veneers.

I have never had warriors bedecked with war paint paddle through swamps in search of me with murderous intent, thank God, and I trust that I never shall. I have, once only, seen an African with red dye smeared all over his naked scrawny body, but he was a reasonably harmless lunatic who was amusing himself by briefly terrorising the kitchen staff in the house of a friend late one night in Nigeria. The dye from the African padauk is just as impressive as that obtained from the 'true camwood'. It looks like blood and it feels like blood and it probably tastes like blood. In the dark ages it adorned tribesmen out to settle a score or two with their neighbours in areas where there was a shortage of the other camwood. When the bark of the tree is slashed, the stuff oozes out copiously, thick and sticky, blood-red and gory. Even the most ghoulish of little boys back in my childhood could hardly have failed to be satisfied with it.

* * * * *

WHILE I HAVE never seen a 'Monkey Can't Climb' tree struck by lightning, neither have I ever seen one that even bore the faintest of scars from a strike at some time in the distant past. But life in some harsh environments among some strange people have imbued me with a regrettable cynicism and I remain somewhat sceptical of most ancient fables. My extensive travels have taken me among literally millions of trees in my life, and I have only ever witnessed actual lightning strikes on trees half-a-dozen times. It is true that I have often seen burnt-out shells of trees on the day following a storm and the tell-tale scars of strikes on many other trees, but these were, after all, but a tiny percentage of the whole. There have, therefore, been plenty of other species of trees that I could have placed in the lightning-inviolate category. Tall trees that stand out high above their neighbours are those most at risk, regardless of species, and movingui is always of modest height.

As to the monkey business, well . . .

I was standing on the edge of a small farm clearing in the middle of the forest. Right in the centre of the clearing, among the young cassava, was a tall and graceful movingui. Sitting right on top of its crown was a male collared mangabey monkey. His chestnut head-piece gleamed in the sunshine and the hooded eyes in his cheeky face were concentrated on the leaves and flowers with which he was stuffing himself.

I thought about the old legend. How did he get up there? I wondered. There was not another tree anywhere near him. He could only have climbed up the trunk, and yet the bole was not only bereft of branches for all of its length right up to the crown but it was as shiny-smooth as any movingui I had ever seen.

It was certainly not the first time I had seen a monkey in a movingui tree, for many of them seemed to have a particular fondness for the leaves of this species, but such occasions were always in a closed-canopy situation where they could leap or swing from the branches of the surrounding trees. I had to confess to myself that I had never seen a monkey up a movingui tree so isolated from its neighbours until now. Perhaps, after all, I really *had* begun to believe the legend. Now, though, one more delightful old fable had crumbled to ashes before my eyes.

The mangabey spotted me. He stopped eating and stared across the clearing at me. Then he turned around, lifting his long tail, exposing his skinny grey buttocks to me. He defecated explosively, liquidly, contentedly. Then he turned back round to face me again. He yattered at me, the harsh chattering echoing over the clearing. 'Ex Africa semper aliquid novi,' he seemed to be shouting at me, 'So put that in your pipe and smoke it.'

And right smug he looked about it, too.

Chapter 17

The Grey Men

Botanical Name	–	*Triplochiton scleroxylon*
Trade Name	–	Obeche
Other Names	–	Arere (Nigeria) Samba (Ivory Coast) Ayous (Cameroon)
Distribution	–	Tropical West Africa
Timber	–	Creamy white to pale yellow. Fine of texture. Rather featureless, but on occasion interlocked grain will produce faint stripe when quarter-sawn. Dries easily. Very easy to work with all tools.
Commercial Uses	–	Virtually all types of interior work; soundboards for organs.

Frequently I find myself being asked which of all West Africa's tree species I consider to be my favourite. I shall never have an easier question to answer. It is, without question, the mighty obeche, the 'Grey Man' of Yoruba folklore.

My first job in Africa was cataloguing all the tree species growing in a certain forest reserve in northern Ondo in Nigeria. I could not have wished for a more pleasant introduction to the tropics or a more beautiful area in which to be based.

In those middle years of the 20th century, Ondo was a very large province indeed. It stretched from the foetid mangrove swamps of the Gulf of Guinea to the very fringe of the great belt of savannah that separated the Sahara from the rainforests of the equator. It was a province of sudden and startling contrasts. The extreme south consisted of the usual network of mist-wreathed creeks and sluggish waterways choked with mangroves, and, to the immediate north of this, the brooding rainforests filled with all the traditional 'heavies' such as ekki and opepe, as well as other moisture-loving species such as abura and lagoswood. Some 40 miles north of the coastal areas, everything changed with startling abruptness: crags and rock outcrops and bluffs suddenly appeared, jutting upward from the surrounding forests. The cloying humidity of the southern rainforests cleared almost magically, to be replaced by a refreshing crispness, or, if not quite crispness, something at least akin to it, with even patches of elephant grass and sawgrass hoving into view in places to break up the monotony of the bottle-green of the rainforest.

Tree-species changes could be just as abrupt and dramatic. This point marked the edge of the southern fringe of the semi-deciduous forests. Further north of this, less and less of the traditional 'heavies' of the coastal regions would be seen, and one encountered species that rarely or never found their way into the coastal forests. One of those was the obeche.

Obeche is a great colonizer and a very gregarious species. One will come across single specimens scattered throughout the northern parts of the true rainforests, but it is not a species that enjoys its own company in the manner of, say, iroko. It tends to grow in stands, almost always in places where subsistence farmers in the distant past had gouged out great chunks of the forest and then – when the thin topsoil had become so depleted of nutrients that it was unable to support foodcrops any more – abandoned their farms. Given such circumstances, and in a climate favourable to its growth, obeche would move in to fill the gap.

While I have come across obeche growing throughout the evergreen forests, it has invariably been as single specimens in mixture with other species. It has never looked comfortable to me in such an environment. Few trees ever attained the sizes or bole shapes they achieved in the drier lands of the north. The boles were often skinny and sinuous. Indeed, trees growing in such an environment always seemed to me to have an air of soggy dejection about them, as though they were fully aware of just how out of place they were in those southern climes – interlopers in a land of hostile strangers.

Where you find one obeche tree, you are liable to come across dozens, or even hundreds. It is a tree that grows best in the semi-deciduous area to the immediate north of the evergreen forests, especially in the proximity of crags and rock formations where it can grow to quite outstanding proportions. Magnificent specimens have been encountered by me in south-central Liberia, Ivory Coast, Ghana, Nigeria and Cameroon, although I have also found large pockets of obeche well outside the accepted northern limit of this semi-deciduous zone, usually in the damper and more favourable soil conditions bordering the water courses that meandered through the orchard savannah. These water courses often dried up during the months following the end of the rains, but even in very prolonged dry seasons enough moisture would be retained in the soil to keep the trees alive until the next brief rains came. Such pockets of high forest were generally surrounded by seas of tall grass stretching as far as the eye could see, and animals never encountered in the wet forests bordering the coastal regions would frequently be seen within them by day and heard calling by night.

Obeche in those unnaturally dry conditions, however, while impressive to look at, particularly when seen growing against a background of elephant grass and scrubby savannah trees, tended to be rather stunted of bole. They were at the extreme northern limit of their range. They were straight enough and diameters were generally good, but bole lengths would seldom exceed two-thirds of those to be found on trees growing in optimum conditions to the south. Their timber was also much more liable to attack by blue-staining agencies from the moment of felling, and the infamous 'inherent grub' so dreaded by timber men gave constant problems to log exporters.

Of all the non-mahogany trees of Africa, however, none has ever come close to the popularity of obeche as a timber tree since the end of the Second World War. When seen in its proper setting, it is a truly beautiful tree and, for such a colossus, there is a strange sort of grace about it that one more readily associates with smaller, more slender species. It towers to a height of over 50 metres and one giant I saw in Cameroon measured 3.5 metres above the buttresses. When later felled, it was found to be perfectly sound throughout and I was later informed that the Italian timber people who had purchased it had the butt log preserved and placed in a timber museum somewhere in Italy.

While young specimens have low, rather blunt buttresses, old mature trees usually have well developed buttresses which often reach high up the bole. At this stage in the tree's life, the flanges are flat and thin. The bole is straight and cylindrical in good conditions; less so at the southern extremity of the tree's range, when it will often be found to be rather angular and heavily ridged. The bark is an ash-grey, becoming a silver-grey in the more open forests where the sun lights on it, and in very old trees it can be quite scaly.

The crown, though surprisingly small in area for such a large tree, is dense and rounded, with heavy, closely packed branches which are often covered in lichens and orchids and a general assortment of epiphytes. The leaves are extraordinarily beautiful, similar in shape and size to those of the Canadian maple. Indeed, in the dry season, just before the leaves fall, they often exhibit the same colour changes as those of the maple, with gold and red and bronze and orange and purple hues. The tree flowers in December at the height of the dry season, usually after the leaves have fallen. The flowers, measuring about two centimetres across, are profuse and very pretty, with petals of a delicate pink with deep-purple centres. The fruit is very reminiscent of that of the maple, except that it consists of only a single seed attached to a single veined wing about 5 centimetres long.

Obeche timber is generally white in colour with, on occasion, a pale yellowish tinge to it. Its popularity has been quite remarkable, considering its unfavourable qualities. It is neither strong nor durable, it is subject to most forms of fungal and insect attack. Particularly large diameter logs have a stong tendency towards brittle heart, and the heartwood was found to be resistant to preservative treatment. However, a surge in demand for white 'hardwoods', combined with a decline in the availability of traditional favourites such as ash after the Second World War, resulted in a closer and more careful scrutiny of West African species that, in the past, would barely have warranted a second thought by the timber men of Europe. The enormous quantities of obeche to be found growing on the Coast naturally attracted their attention and soon established it as the most popular of all of West Africa's white rainforest timbers. It is a position which it holds to this day.

The wood dried rapidly and with very little degradation taking place. Easy to work with all manner of tools, it nailed, glued and polished without difficulty and was found to be ideal for all manner of interior joinery. Perhaps most important of all, it made excellent plywood. Where ripple figure was found to be present, it even produced a most attractive sliced veneer.

The timber is very light – when dried, it is about half the weight of African mahogany – and it has always been favoured by African carpenters in the hinterland, especially for such household items such as chairs, stools, bedframes, tables and shelves. It was also commonly made into juju masks. In some of the drier areas to the north of the true rainforests, such as on the northern reaches of the Anambra River in Nigeria, canoes were made from it, though so perishable was the timber that these never lasted long. However, the great advantage from the bush carpenter's point of view was the ease with which the timber could be worked. It required neither too much time nor too much effort to knock up a replacement.

Particularly lazy house-builders who required doors for their huts did not even have to go to the trouble of pitsawing a fallen tree into planks to make one. Indeed, he had no need to fell a tree for the purpose. The massive thin root flanges were ideal for doors and could be hacked off from the standing tree and used without the necessity of doing further work on them. An even less arduous way of making doors was to use the thick but pliable bark which could be removed with astonishing ease from the trunk of a newly fallen tree in large unbroken sheets. In some parts of Cameroon it was also used in the making of complete walls and roofs for huts. Having slept many times in huts made almost entirely from sheets of obeche bark, I found them most pleasant places in which to live and cool even during the hottest times of the year.

Another 'Grey Man' of those same moist semi-deciduous forests – and one which can be found frequently in association with obeche – is limba, or *Terminalia superba*. The trade name for limba usually varies according to its country of origin; in the old British colonial countries it is usually called 'white afara', while in French-speaking countries such as Ivory Coast and Cameroon it is called 'fraké'.

Limba cannot be confused with any other tree in Africa. It is very tall, slender in proportion to its height, and ruler-straight. It can grow to 50 metres high, without a twig or a blemish of any sort on its beautifully cylindrical trunk right up to the small storied crown of whorled branches which jut out horizontally from the bole high up there next to the blue of the sky. Everything about the limba tree has an almost geometric beauty about it and its appeal is therefore to engineers rather than the naturalist. It is perfection personified in its design. Even the bole taper is so slight as to be invisible from ground level. When standing, it looks for all the world like some giant silver-boled telegraph pole when the sun gleams upon it in the openness of the semi-deciduous forests. In maturity it has high-reaching, thin, plank buttresses which, in their sharply angular steepness and precise uniformity, emphasise the tree's appearance of geometric perfection.

It is little wonder that the early botanists named it as they did: while '*Terminalia*' simply refers to the way in which the leaves are clustered in terminal tufts, the '*superba*' refers to its imposing habit.

In the gloom of the forest the bark has a light-grey appearance, though in direct sunlight – in common with obeche – it acquires a distinctly silvery aspect. The rather misleading trade name of 'white afara' refers, in fact, to the colour of the bark and not to the colour of the timber, which can be grey, chocolate-brown or black, or – more often – a mixture of all three. (The closely related species *Terminalia ivorensis*, often called 'black afara' by log exporters because of its bark colour, has pale yellowish-green timber.)

Limba is much favoured by the foresters of the Coast. It regenerates easily and prolifically, and it is therefore much used as a plantation tree in mixture with such exotics as teak. It grows very rapidly and, once the seedling has survived its first two or three critical years in the plantation, few insects appear to attack it.

The timber of limba, which is in considerable demand on the world market, varies greatly from a lustrous grey to straw-colour, and timber of a greyish-green hue is not uncommon. Dark-grey, dark-brown and ebony-black streaks and washes will often be found in the heartwood, and this effect is most commonly to be found in very large logs. The incidence of these very dark colourations seems to be much higher in certain areas than in others, and in the French-speaking countries it is common to divide such timber into two grades – 'limba blanc', in which two-thirds or more of the log is of a light colour, and 'limba noir', in which most of the log is seen to be dark in colour. The timber is close-grained and generally straight of grain, but the occasional log will be found to have wavy grain which produces a most attractive figure.

It is easy to work with all kinds of tools and it kiln-dries without any problems. Although not at all durable, it is much in demand for virtually all forms of interior carpentry, from the making of coffins to high-class furniture, panelling and sliced veneer. Logs with black heart are much in demand for the latter purpose, for it is extremely decorative, while plain timber is used for utility plywood.

Limba is a tree of a type of grace and beauty that is different from that of the obeche which could only have been formed by Mother Nature, for obeche gives an impression of ruggedness to go with the beauty in the stumpy, gnarled branches and occasional lumps and knobs on the buttresses. Limba has none of those imperfections and looks as though it must have been designed by the Master Architect Himself. But both species, in their own unique and quite different ways, add style and class to their particular habitat.

I have one abiding memory of limba that has nothing to do with the symmetrical perfection of its form or the quality of its timber: it has more to do with one of West Africa's most common creatures, a bird that can be found in abundance wherever the limba tree flourishes, from Sierra Leone to Cameroon.

The African grey parrot seems to have a special fondness for the limba tree. Wherever possible, it will choose this species as its nesting tree. No one really knows why this should be so: some tribal folklore would have it that it is because the colour of the limba's bark reminds the parrot of the various shades of grey and silver in its own plumage. Others believe that, because parrots always nest at the very tops of trees, the limba is ideal for them as the smooth, branchless bole gives no purchase or foothold for predators wishing to raid their nests. Whatever the reason, the attraction is not the fruit of the limba (a tiny, winged nut) for, although parrots eat most types of nuts, seeds and fruit, they seem little attracted to that of the limba, even though it grows in abundance. In the wild, the African grey parrot seems to be especially attracted to scarlet fruit, such as that of the oil plam.

African grey parrots were a common sight in every market along the Coast, usually tethered by the foot or in crude wicker cages. Nearly all had claws missing, for the usual method of catching them was by iron traps set by waterholes in the forest. My own introduction to this delightful bird had nothing to do with either traps or markets. It came about as I watched a very tall limba tree being felled. As soon as it hit the ground, the fellers set to work with their axes removing the branches from the crown. As I was about to leave, one of the workers beckoned to me. I scrambled through the tangle of branches towards him. Two baby parrots had been ejected from a hole near to the top of the tree. They were quite dead, killed by the impact. I thrust my hand inside. In the bare unlined nest cavity there was one survivor, completely naked and about the size of a house sparrow. No doubt it had been protected from the force of the fall by having somehow remained inside the hole for it was still moving feebly, but I had given it little chance of lasting out the day. Nevertheless, I took it home with me. Miraculously, a diet which consisted solely of palm oil diluted with coconut water, kept the little creature going for the first crucial week.

'Parrot' became a most handsome bird and she now lives somewhere in England with my sister and her husband. She is nearly half a century old, but she looks and acts like a maiden half her age. Her repertoire is quite remarkable, and occasionally scandalous. It ranges from bird songs and animal sounds to telephones ringing, snatches of human conversation and the whistling of obscure Aberdonian folk tunes. She can mimic human physical actions as well as sounds, and her re-enactment of my father's bodily contortions while she delivers a perfect rendition of his bronchial smoker's cough, would win her my Oscar nomination any day of the week.

She has been gone from Africa's shores for well over 40 years now, but even after all this time the fleeting shadow of a patrolling kestrel overhead as she sits out on the patio of a summer evening will send her cowering in terror to the bottom of the cage as the ghosts of ancient Africa come rushing back to haunt her.

In the semi-deciduous forests of southern Nigeria, Ghana and the Ivory Coast I have come across another species which has been in considerable demand as a timber tree since the Second World War. This is bété, or *Mansonia altissima*, and it has been in close proximity to obeche that I have most often come across it in those countries. However, bété would rarely be found growing as a single tree within stands of obeche, for it tended to grow *en masse* in pure stands wherever one happened to find it.

Bété is a straight-stemmed tree, neither very tall nor very thick of frame. It grows to a height of around 30 metres and a diameter of about 0.75 of a metre, and its timber has become much valued as a sutstitute for American black walnut, which it closely resembles in appearance. The heartwood is of a dark-grey to chocolate hue, with a pronounced purplish tinge. In at least some of its properties – such as its working qualities – it is regarded by many as being superior to the American black walnut. It is much used as a decorative timber in high quality cabinet work, radio and television sets, dashboards for cars, many types of musical instruments, and even as an occasional substitute for European walnut. It is very durable indeed and resistant to preservatives. It dries well, polishes beautifully, and produces an excellent finish. One major drawback – not always mentioned by log exporters trying to promote their timbers – is the fact that the dust produced through machining and sanding of this species can give great irritation to the eyes, nose and throat, and it has been known to cause dermatitis. The bark, too, is highly poisonous.

There are two other main species which I have found to be in reasonable quantity during my years of work in obeche forests, only one of which has ever made any kind of mark on the timber trade, and even then its impact upon the markets of Europe has been so muted as to be barely discernible. Odoko (*Scottellia coriacea*) occurs in southern Nigeria – a small tree by rainforest standards, rarely attaining a height of more than 20 metres. It is a very slender, rather insignificant tree and tends to be overlooked among its giant neighbours. A few good-sized specimens have been taken by European buyers in the past, mainly because its timber looks quite like European beech, with the same distinctive 'silver grain'. Although it is not in the slightest durable, it takes preservatives with the greatest of ease and so has been used as a beech substitute in many of the latter's traditional uses: shoe heels, clog soles, hair-brush backs, musical instruments, food containers, and so on. Owing to its quite astonishing resistance to wear, its pale-yellow timber has also been used for flooring.

The greatest use made of it in the African hinterland was by witchdoctors. Of all the rainforest trees, none held greater significance in tribal medicine than the odoko. When a witchdoctor feared that his juju charms and amulets were losing their protective powers, these could be restored by rubbing them with an ointment made from the bark and leaves of a young odoko mixed with palm oil. Most of the top witchdoctors considered it to be infallible.

Ayinre (*Albizia spp.*) was another common tree in the semi-deciduous obeche forests of Nigeria. Of the five main species of *Albizia* scattered throughout the centre of Africa from west coast to east, only two came regularly to my notice: *A. zigia* and *A. ferruginea*. The former, generally called 'small ayinre' by the forest people, was common and gregarious among secondary formations in the moister parts of the semi-deciduous zone. It was a small tree and tended to be of rather poor shape. *A. ferruginea*, usually referred to as 'big ayinre', was quite a large forest tree, occasionally attaining a height of 35 metres. Its heavily branched spreading crown with the feathery foliage, the abundant long and papery carmine seed pods hanging from its branches in clusters, and its densely shaggy bark made is a most noticeable tree. What made 'big ayinre' even more conspicuous was its solitary disposition. As one walked through the forest, one would suddenly encounter a large specimen standing there incongruously in all its sprawling untidiness among the statuesque, structured perfection of the obeche and limba giants around it. One could almost imagine them looking down their aristocratic noses at this unwanted intruder in their midst.

Ayinre timber is of a rather coarse-looking dark-brown hue, and indeed the texture is also coarse. It is, however, very durable, and it has even found a use in Europe for marine installations, railway sleepers and heavy duty flooring. It has never, though, been regarded with such favour as to excite more than a passing interest even in peak years. There has always been a sufficiency of other 'heavies' from Africa – such as ekki – to fill this niche. Even the forest African would seldom bother to exercise himself mentally or physically by pitsawing a windblown specimen into planks if something better was available, even though ayinre is not, in fact, too difficult to saw.

Yet the ayinres, big and small, have always interested me, for they have several remarkable qualities, not the least of these connected with the foliage. Most unusually for rain-forest trees, the leaves exhibit distinct sleep movements with the onset of darkness. They also produce a lather when rubbed together in water, for they contain saponin. In the forest they were often used as a soap substitute, and I have used them as such myself. But most interesting of all to me was the association that ayinre had with what was, perhaps, the most curious of all the inhabitants of the rainforest and – quite unarguably – the most cuddly-looking of all.

The first creature of the African wild I ever held in my hand was the bush baby. It was infested with tiny ants and on the verge of death. I had picked it up at the foot of a large tree in the heart of the forest where it had quite obviously broken its back, possibly through mistiming its jump in the high tops far above me. Although I had read about bush babies and seen pictures of them, this was my first actual encounter with one, so, having put the poor little mite out of its misery, I studied it.

In body length, it was no more than 20 centimetres long, with a tail longer than its body and a strange but quite beautiful bushy part at the tip. Its hind legs were slightly longer than its front legs, with fingers and toes flattened at the ends and pads of thick skin on them, presumably as an aid to gripping branches. Its ears were very large and bat-like. Its general coloration was a sort of light tan, with a dark grey tail and a very light – almost white – face mask. But its most remarkable features were its eyes. They were huge and cocoabrown and luminous and soulful. Even as they dimmed rapidly in death, the depth of sadness within those great liquid orbs would have melted the stoniest heart.

Bush babies share a common ancestry with apes and humans. They acquired their name from the early British explorers to Africa who likened their calls to those of an excited child. They feed primarily on insects, mainly dung beetles and caterpillars, but they will also take mice, lizards, nestlings, fruits, seeds and – when they can find a colony of stingless bees – they are very partial to honey. They like flowers, too, and are one of the few mammals to fertilize flowers by the transfer of pollen as they feed.

They can spring prodigious distances from branch to branch in their quest for food. A leap of more than 7 metres has been recorded, a remarkable feat for such a small animal. Bush babies are completely nocturnal, and during the day they sleep – often in colonies of twenty or more – in some enclosed space such as a hollow tree trunk. They are easily caught, make charming pets and are easily tamed. A common daytime practice is to smoke them out of their sleeping quarters in hollow trees, having covered up the exit holes in advance. The forest African employs an even wilier practice during the hours of darkness. Bush babies cannot resist palm wine, so containers of the drink are left out at night in areas known to have a bush baby population. In the morning the little revellers are easily picked up as they lie in drunken slumber around the scene of their previous night's debauchery.

The wet season, when food is abundant, is a good time for bush babies, but long dry spells – which can occur in those northerly forests with surprising frequency – can create havoc. When food is scarce, then the ayinre tree becomes vital to them, for they depend almost exclusively on its honey-like sap to survive at such times. Without this strange tree, it is doubtful if those delightful little creatures could continue to exist. In really hard times, the ayinre tree is their sole source of nourishment.

*   *   *   *   *

THERE IS AN aura of tranquillity about obeche forests that I have never experienced anywhere else. I have worked among the obeche trees in places as far apart as the Putu Range in Liberia and the borders of the pygmy forests in eastern Cameroon. They were all tranquil places, and none more so than the beautiful forests of Ondo and Kabba in Nigeria. Pretty little duikers emerged from them as darkness approached, their white stumps of tails flickering nervously in the brief West African gloaming. The handsome red bushbuck with the bold white stripes along his back and sides browsed quietly among the trees beside the streams, and the pre-historic armour-plated pangolin plodded his way serenely through the undergrowth in search of ant and termite colonies. It was in forests such as these that one could be sure of finding the lovable bush baby.

However, tranquillity is not always what it seems. In 1940 a terrible outbreak of yellow fever swept through the African forests and the surrounding bush country, wiping out whole communities of people. It took a long time before it abated, and even longer before the boffins tracked down the source of it to the delightful, cuddly little bush baby. It was proved beyond doubt to be a prime carrier of the virus, harbouring it without ever becoming ill from the infection itself. Mosquitoes picked up the virus from the bush babies and passed it on to humans.

Although stringent inoculation programmes were enforced for those intending to visit tropical Africa, virtually ensuring immunity, it is a fact that the bush baby has been accorded a new respect since those terrible years. Big sad eyes and a winsome appearance are no guarantee of purity in the cauldron of the White Man's Grave, as any hardened Old Coaster could have confirmed.

There can surely have been no greater betrayal in the history of mankind. Even in the Garden of Eden the serpent came in such a guise, not as a cuddly little creature that looked as though it would be more at home in a child's playpen. No one could have doubted the intention of the serpent.

Except, of course, that fool Adam.

Epilogue

'I HAVE FALLEN under the spell of the African forests, and it takes all the colour out of other kinds of living.' So said Mary Kingsley towards the end of the 19th century on her return to England from the west coast of Africa. Halfway through the 20th century I went out there myself as a young forester and I, too, fell under their spell. It has been a love affair that has endured to this day.

The mechanics of man have destroyed those wonderful forests. The arrival of the chainsaw, banishing the axe instantly to the museum, sealed their fate. In short order the peace of the forests, from the Grain Coast in the west to the Bight of Biafra in the east, was shattered by the eldritch dirges of those evil-smelling mechanical monsters, and vast swathes of forest that would have taken many months to fell by the old traditional methods were now being flattened by the chainsaw on a daily basis. The age of innocence had gone, and the ancient rainforests of Africa were heading fast for extinction.

As we begin the new millennium, the situation is critical. There is no doubt whatever about that. It has long been obvious that the flagrant plunder of this world's greatest natural resource would have dire consequences for the environment. But it is not enough just to blame the logger: like the proprieter of a brothel, he only exists because there are plenty around who are prepared to pay for his commodity. The politicians, black and white, who could long ago have done something about the situation, are the ones at whose door the blame must lie. By their self-serving greed and blatant

211

corruption, they have betrayed the people over whose lands they had been elected to throw the mantle of protection.

Yet all is not lost. There is among the young of today all over the world an awareness about the dangers of environmental abuse that never existed in my generation. Today's generation are also brash and outspoken, which we never were. We meekly suppressed any doubts we may have entertained about the morality of what was going on around us. None of us would have had the nerve to squat in the crown of a tree night after freezing night or to have lived in a muddy hole in the ground in an attempt to publicize our concerns. We would have been too worried about what the neighbours thought of us.

It is with today's generation that our hopes for the future – as embodied in Mary Kingsley's beloved rainforests – must lie.